Don Webster

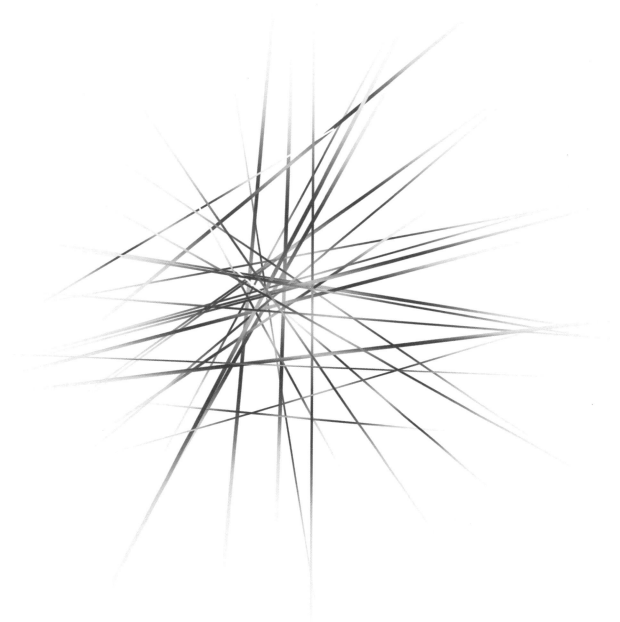

# ESSENTIALS

## GCSE Physical Education
### Workbook

# Contents

## Body Systems

4    The Skeleton

5    Vertebral Column

6    Joints

8    Muscles

10    Respiratory System

12    Circulatory System

14    Blood Pressure

15    Effects of Exercise

## Fitness and Training

16    Reasons for Exercise

20    Principles of Training

21    Goal Setting

22    Training Threshold

23    Aerobic and Anaerobic Training

24    Training Methods

28    Programmes of Exercise

29    Training Requirements

30    Training Sessions

31    Effects of Exercise

33    Testing

## Factors Affecting Performance

36    Factors Affecting Performance

40    Skill

42    Drugs in Sport

# Contents

## Participation in Sport

| | | |
|---|---|---|
| **44** | Taking Part | |
| **46** | Participation | |
| **48** | The Way to Play | |
| **50** | Modern Technology | |
| **52** | Training Aids | |
| **53** | Playing Safe | |
| **55** | Lifting and Carrying | |

## Issues in Sport

| | | |
|---|---|---|
| **56** | Sponsorship | |
| **58** | Media | |
| **60** | Politics | |
| **62** | Sporting Behaviour | |
| **64** | Sporting Status | |
| **66** | Discrimination | |

## Organisation in Sport

| | | |
|---|---|---|
| **70** | Sport in School | |
| **71** | Facilities | |
| **72** | Organisation of Sport | |
| **74** | Promoting Excellence | |
| **76** | Promoting International Sport | |
| **77** | Funding for Sport | |

## Exam-Style Questions

| | | |
|---|---|---|
| **78** | Multiple choice questions | |
| **80** | Short Answer questions | |
| **87** | Analysis questions | |

# The Skeleton

## The Skeleton and its Functions

**1** What are the main functions of the skeleton? Tick the correct options.

   **A** Blood formation ◯         **B** Protection ◯

   **C** Breathing ◯         **D** Femur ◯

   **E** Blood flow ◯         **F** Movement ◯

   **G** Support ◯         **H** Warmth ◯

**2** Fill in the missing words to complete the following sentences.

   **a)** You can't _____ or bend without bones.

   **b)** The skeleton gives you _____ and holds vital _____ in place.

**3** How many bones are in the body? Tick the correct option.

   **A** 205 ◯         **B** 206 ◯

   **C** 207 ◯         **D** 208 ◯

**4** Bones are classified into four types. What type of bone are the following?

   **a)** Femur _____

   **b)** Scapula _____

   **c)** Phalanges _____

   **d)** Vertebrae _____

   **e)** Humerus _____

**5** The following diagram shows the two different parts of the skeleton. Match **A** and **B** with the labels **1** and **2**. Enter the appropriate number in the boxes provided.

   **A** Appendicular skeleton ◯

   **B** Axial skeleton ◯

   1 ⟶

   2 ⟶

**6** Does the axial or the appendicular skeleton have a large amount of movement?

_____ ▢

## Vertebrae

**1** How many bones are there in the vertebral column? Tick the correct option.

**A** 26 ◯          **B** 27 ◯

**C** 28 ◯          **D** 29 ◯

**2** Other than the coccyx, what are the other four groups of vertebrae called?

a) .......................................................................................................................

b) .......................................................................................................................

c) .......................................................................................................................

d) .......................................................................................................................

**3** What makes the coccyx different from all the other groups of vertebrae?

.......................................................................................................................

**4** Fill in the missing word to complete the following sentence.

The small discs between the vertebrae are made of ............................................ .

**5** **a)** What are the two vertebrae at the top of the column called? Tick the correct option.

**A** Sacral and lumbar ◯          **B** Atlas and appendicular ◯

**C** Axis and appendicular ◯          **D** Atlas and axis ◯

**b)** What do these two vertebrae allow the head to do?

.......................................................................................................................

## Functions of the Column

**6** List the three functions of the spinal column.

a) .......................................................................................................................

b) .......................................................................................................................

c) .......................................................................................................................

# Joints

## Types of Joint

**1** Draw lines between the boxes to match the type of joint with its amount of movement.

**Type of Joint**

| Fibrous |
| Cartilaginous |
| Synovial |

**Amount of Movement**

| Freely movable |
| Fixed |
| Slightly movable |

## Synovial Joints

**2** List the five types of synovial joint.

a) ....................................................................................................................................

b) ....................................................................................................................................

c) ....................................................................................................................................

d) ....................................................................................................................................

e) ....................................................................................................................................

## Joints

**3** The diagram shows the parts of a synovial joint. Match **A, B, C** and **D** with the labels **1−4**. Enter the appropriate number in the boxes provided.

**A** Outer ligament ◯

**B** Capsule of joint ◯

**C** Synovial membrane ◯

**D** Synovial fluid ◯

1

2

3

4

**4** Is the following statement **true** or **false**?

Ligaments hold bones together but they aren't flexible. ....................................................

## Movement at Joints

**1** Draw lines between the boxes to match the type of joint with how it moves.

| Type of Joint | How it Moves |
|---|---|
| Flexion | Towards centre of body |
| Extension | Joint closing |
| Adduction | Turning round |
| Abduction | Drawing a circle |
| Rotation | Joint opening / straightening |
| Circumduction | Away from centre of body |

**2** Place a tick against the joint that can perform the following types of movement.

|  | Hinge | Ball and Socket | Pivot | Condyloid | Saddle | Gliding |
|---|---|---|---|---|---|---|
| Flexion |  |  |  |  |  | **A small amount of these types of movement** |
| Extension |  |  |  |  |  | |
| Abduction |  |  |  |  |  | |
| Adduction |  |  |  |  |  | |
| Rotation |  |  |  |  |  | |
| Circumduction |  |  |  |  |  | |

## Joints and Muscles

**3** Circle the correct options in the following sentences.

a) **Tendons / Ligaments** attach muscle to bone.

b) **Tendons / Ligaments** attach bone to bone.

**4** Give two conditions that joints can suffer from.

a) _____

b) _____

# Muscles

## Muscles

**1 a)** What are the three types of muscle found in the body?

**i)** ......................................................................................................

**ii)** ......................................................................................................

**iii)** ......................................................................................................

**b)** Which of these muscles is only found in the heart?

......................................................................................................

**2** The diagrams show the positions of muscles. Match **A–K** with the labels **1–11**. Enter the appropriate number in the boxes provided.

**A** Latissimus Dorsi ◯

**B** Gastrocnemius ◯

**C** Abdominals ◯

**D** Biceps ◯

**E** Trapezius ◯

**F** Deltoid ◯

**G** Pectorals ◯

**H** Triceps ◯

**I** Gluteals ◯

**J** Quadriceps ◯

**K** Hamstrings ◯

## How Muscles Work

**3** Draw lines between the boxes to match the muscle with how it works.

| Type of Muscle | How it Works |
|---|---|
| Agonist | Stabilises joint |
| Antagonist | Relaxes to allow movement |
| Synergist | Contracts to create movement |

## Types of Fibre

**1** **a)** How do fast twitch fibres work?

........................................................................................................................

........................................................................................................................

**b)** Name a type of event that fast twitch fibres are best for.

........................................................................................................................

**2** **a)** How do slow twitch fibres work?

........................................................................................................................

........................................................................................................................

**b)** Name a type of event that slow twitch fibres are best for.

........................................................................................................................

## Types of Contraction

**3** Circle the correct options in the following sentences.

**a)** During isometric contractions the muscle fibres **change length / stay the same length** and the bones **move / don't move**.

**b)** During isotonic contractions the muscle fibres **change length / stay the same length** and the bones **move / don't move**.

**4** What happens to muscle fibres during concentric contractions?

........................................................................................................................

**5** What happens to muscle fibres during eccentric contractions?

........................................................................................................................

**6** **a)** How do the biceps muscles contract during an arm curl? Tick the correct option.

**A** Eccentrically ⬭ **B** Concentrically ⬭

**b)** How do the triceps muscles lengthen during an arm curl? Tick the correct option.

**A** Eccentrically ⬭ **B** Concentrically ⬭

# Respiratory System

## Breathing

**1** List the three main parts of the respiratory system.

**a)** ........................................................................................................................

**b)** ........................................................................................................................

**c)** ........................................................................................................................

**2** **a)** Explain what the intercostal muscles do during inspiration.

........................................................................................................................

**b)** Explain what happens to the diaphragm during inspiration.

........................................................................................................................

**3** What two actions squeeze the air out during expiration?

**a)** ........................................................................................................................

**b)** ........................................................................................................................

## Gaseous Exchange

**4** Fill in the missing words to complete the following sentence.

Gaseous exchange is the ........................................... of oxygen and carbon dioxide between

the ........................................ and the ........................................ that surround the alveoli.

**5** Choose the correct words from the options given to complete the sentences below.

| | | | |
|---|---|---|---|
| **oxygen** | **capillaries** | **white** | **uptake** |
| **red** | **carbon dioxide** | **alveoli** | **veins** |

**a)** ........................................... from the air is passed through the thin walls of the alveoli to the

........................................... cells in the blood. This process is called oxygen ........................................... .

**b)** ........................................... is passed from the blood through the thin walls of the

........................................... into the ........................................... .

## Gaseous Exchange (cont.)

**1** What does gaseous exchange depend on? Tick the correct options.

**A** Vital capacity ☐          **B** Minute volume ☐

**C** Inspirit ☐          **D** Vital incapacity ☐

**E** Tidal volume ☐          **F** $TO_2$ ☐

**G** Respiratory rate ☐          **H** $VO_2$ ☐

**2** What is vital capacity?

## Response to Exercise

**3** Fill in the missing words to complete the following sentences.

**a)** Aerobic exercise is a _____ intensity activity. It uses _____

to produce _____ .

**b)** Aerobic exercise produces two waste products called _____ and

_____ . It can be carried out for _____ periods of time.

It only needs a short _____ period.

**c)** Anaerobic exercise is a _____ intensity activity. It uses _____
to produce energy.

**d)** Anaerobic exercise's main waste product is _____ acid, which is poisonous.

This is caused by a lack of oxygen, known as oxygen _____ .

**4** Complete the following equations.

**a)** Aerobic respiration

Glucose + [＿＿＿＿＿] = [＿＿＿＿＿] + [＿＿＿＿＿]

**b)** Anaerobic respiration

[＿＿＿＿＿] = [＿＿＿＿＿] + a bit of [＿＿＿＿＿]

# Circulatory System

## Circulatory System

**1** Fill in the missing words to complete the following sentence.

The circulatory system pumps blood round the body in a ........................................

of ........................................ pathway.

**2** Name the three main parts of the circulatory system.

**a)** ........................................ **b)** ........................................ **c)** ........................................

## The Heart

**3** The diagram shows the parts of the heart. Match **A–L** with the labels **1–12**. Enter the appropriate number in the boxes provided.

**A** Right atrium ⬭

**B** Semi-lunar valve ⬭

**C** Inferior vena cava ⬭

**D** Left ventricle ⬭

**E** Pulmonary vein ⬭

**F** Superior vena cava ⬭

**G** Left atrium ⬭

**H** Tricuspid valve ⬭

**I** Mitral valve ⬭

**J** Pulmonary artery ⬭

**K** Right ventricle ⬭

**L** Aorta ⬭

**4 a)** What part of the heart sends blood to the body?

........................................................................................................

**b)** What part of the heart receives blood from the body?

........................................................................................................

# Circulatory System

## Pulse

**1** What kind of wave is a pulse beat?

_____

**2** In what type of vessel is a pulse beat found? Tick the correct option.

**A** Capillary ◯        **B** Vein ◯

**C** Pulmonary ◯        **D** Artery ◯

**3** How long should a pulse beat usually be measured for? Tick the correct option.

**A** 30 seconds ◯        **B** 45 seconds ◯

**C** 1 minute ◯        **D** 3 minutes ◯

**4** A pulse beat is measured at the radial artery. Where is this point?

_____

## Blood Vessels

**5** Circle the correct options in the following sentences.

**a)** The **pulmonary / systemic** circuit carries blood from the heart to the body and back to the heart.

**b)** The **pulmonary / systemic** circuit carries blood from the heart to the lungs and back to the heart.

**6** Fill in the missing words to complete the following sentences.

**a)** _____ carry blood away from the heart. They have thick

_____ walls.

**b)** _____ carry blood back to the heart. They have thinner, less

_____ walls.

**c)** Capillaries are found where _____ and _____ meet.

Capillaries are very _____; they only allow blood to pass through one

_____ at a time. Gas _____ takes place through

capillary walls.

# Blood Pressure

## Measuring Blood Pressure

1 What is used to measure blood pressure besides a battery-powered monitor?

........................................................................................................................................................

2 What blood pressure measurements are taken? Tick the correct options.

    **A** Diastemic ⬭                **B** Diastolic ⬭

    **C** Systolic ⬭                  **D** Systemic ⬭

## Blood and its Functions

3 Give the four principal components of blood.

    **a)** ...................................................     **b)** ...................................................

    **c)** ...................................................     **d)** ...................................................

4 Draw lines between the boxes to match the substance with the direction that blood transports it around the body.

| Substance | Direction |
|---|---|
| Heat | From the lungs to all body tissue |
| Waste products | From body tissue to the lungs |
| Oxygen | From the small intestine to all parts of the body |
| Carbon dioxide | From all body tissue to the kidneys |
| Nutrients | From the muscles to the skin |

5 Which part of blood…

    **a)** produces antitoxins to fight poisons and antibodies to fight disease? ..................................

    **b)** aids clotting? ..................................

    **c)** destroys harmful organisms? ..................................

6 What is fibrinogen used for?

........................................................................................................................................................

## Long Term Effects of Exercise

**1** Exercise has long term effects on the body. Circle the correct options in the following sentences.

**a)** The heart's size and strength **increase / decrease**. Stroke volume **increases / decreases** and cardiac output **increases / decreases**.

**b)** The heart's resting rate is **higher / lower** and the return to resting rate is **slower / faster**.

**2** Choose the correct words from the options given to complete the sentences below.

| oxygenated | veins | increase | carbon dioxide | fibres |
|---|---|---|---|---|
| oxygen | capillaries | decrease | deoxygenated | |

**a)** Exercise has long term effects on the blood. The number of red cells _____

and the transportation of _____ improves.

**b)** The return of carbon dioxide is improved and the supply to muscle _____ is

increased. More _____ are made ready for use.

**c)** The return of _____ blood to the heart is improved.

## Short Term Effects of Exercise

**3** Is the following statement **true** or **false**?

The short term effects of exercise on the heart are that both the pulse rate and blood pressure decrease.

_____

**4** Choose the correct words from the options given to complete the sentences below.

| heat | head | skin | soft organs |
|---|---|---|---|
| muscles | fibres | heart | surface |

**a)** Exercise has short term effects on the blood. Blood is diverted from the _____

to the _____.

**b)** Blood rises to the _____ of the _____, making you look red,

and transports _____ from the muscles to the body's surface.

# Reasons for Exercise

## Why do Exercise?

**1** Give four reasons why people take part in exercise.

a) ..................................................................................................................................

b) ..................................................................................................................................

c) ..................................................................................................................................

d) ..................................................................................................................................

## Social and Mental Benefits

**2** Choose the correct words from the options given to complete the sentences below.

| status | earn money | spirit | meet people | rewarding |
|--------|-----------|--------|-------------|-----------|

a) Taking part in exercise can help you ................................................. .

b) Involvement in team sports develops team ................................................. .

c) Some sports carry enhanced social ................................................. .

d) Post-match activities can be ................................................. .

e) Playing some sports can possibly ................................................. .

**3** Choose the correct words from the options given to complete the sentences below.

| fun | self-confidence | perspective | stimulation | goal |
|-----|-----------------|-------------|-------------|------|
| tension | simulation | time | stress | sport |

a) Exercise can reduce ................................. and relieve ................................. .

b) Exercise can provide mental ................................. too.

c) Exercise helps you feel better about yourself and increases ................................. .

d) Exercise can help you look at life with a better ................................. and can be

................................. .

e) Exercise gives you a ................................. to aim for.

# Reasons for Exercise

## Physical Benefits

**1** Are the following statements **true** or **false**?

    **a)** Exercise can help develop an improved body shape and posture. ........................................

    **b)** Exercise has no effect on muscle tone. ........................................

    **c)** Exercise can make bones longer and helps you fight illness and injury. ........................................

**2** Fill in the missing words to complete the following sentences.

    **a)** Physical benefits contribute to a person's physical ........................................ and physical fitness.

    **b)** Fitness is the ability to perform physical activity ........................................ and includes physical

        fitness and ........................................ fitness.

**3** What happens to cardiac output and $O_2$ debt during exercise? Tick the correct option.

    **A** They both increase    ⬭

    **B** Cardiac output increases, $O_2$ debt decreases    ⬭

    **C** They both decrease    ⬭

    **D** Cardiac output decreases, $O_2$ debt increases    ⬭

## Physical Fitness

**4** What is physical fitness?

........................................................................................................................................................

**5** Fill in the boxes with the five main components of physical fitness.

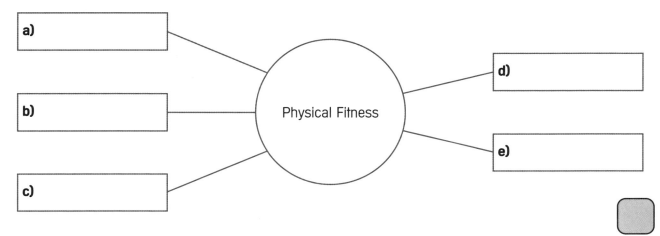

# Reasons for Exercise

## The 5 Components of Physical Fitness

**1** Give the three types of strength.

a) ........................................................................................................................

b) ........................................................................................................................

c) ........................................................................................................................

**2** Give a definition of speed.

........................................................................................................................

........................................................................................................................

**3** Circle the correct options in the following sentence.

Stamina is the ability to perform **light / strenuous** activity over a **long / short** period of time.

**4** What two other terms is stamina known by?

a) .........................................................    b) .........................................................

**5** What do stamina activities need a continuous supply of for the muscles to work? Tick the correct option.

**A** Glucose ◯    **B** Nitrogen ◯

**C** Oxygen ◯    **D** Speed ◯

**6** What two other terms is suppleness known by?

a) .........................................................    b) .........................................................

## Aerobic and Anaerobic Fitness

**7** Draw lines between the boxes to match the type of fitness with its correct description.

**Type of Fitness**

Aerobic fitness

Anaerobic fitness

**Description**

For lower intensity activities
Long periods of time
Gets energy from oxygen

For higher intensity activities
Short periods of time
Gets energy from glucose

## Motor Fitness

**1** What is motor fitness?

_____

_____

_____

**2** Fill in the missing words to complete the following sentences.

**a)** Power is a combination of _____ and _____ working together.

**b)** Agility is the _____ to change _____ quickly.

**c)** _____ is the ability to perform several tasks, each linked together.

**d)** Balance is an awareness of body _____ at any given time.

**e)** Reaction is the time taken to respond to a given _____.

**f)** Attitude is the _____ approach of the performer, sometimes called the will to win.

## Posture

**3** Fill in the missing word to complete the following sentence.

Exercise improves muscle tone around the _____, which contributes to good posture.

**4** How does good posture help the joints?

_____

_____

_____

**5** How does posture help the body? Tick the correct options.

**A** Helps avoid deformity ⃝

**B** Helps in breathing ⃝

**C** Ensures all body parts are misaligned ⃝

**D** Helps improve flexibility ⃝

# Principles of Training

**1** Choose the correct word from the options given to complete the sentence below.

**Distillation**          **Deterioration**          **Diversion**          **Detainment**

The five guiding principles are best remembered as SPORT – Specificity, Progression, Overload,

Reversibility and ................................................., and Tedium.

## The SPORT Principles

**2** Circle the correct options in the following sentences.

**a)** Specificity is training for a specific **time / activity** and a specific type of fitness.

**b)** Progression is adapting to training levels of fitness. It's achieved by a gradual **increase / decrease** in intensity, which creates an overload.

**c)** Reversibility is the effect of **increasing / reducing** the intensity of exercise or **stopping completely / exercising more**.

**d)** Tedium is the effect of training becoming **faster / boring**, which can be overcome by changing **training methods / exercising quicker**.

**3** What does the I in FITT stand for?

........................................................................................................................

**4** Draw lines between the boxes to match the principle with its definition.

| Principle | Definition |
|-----------|------------|
| F | Which exercises are suitable to your chosen sport |
| I | How long you exercise |
| T | How often you exercise |
| T | How hard you exercise |

**5** What is atrophy?

........................................................................................................................

........................................................................................................................

## Setting Targets in Training

**1** Setting goals helps to attain success. What can goals help to show? Tick the correct options.

| | | | | |
|---|---|---|---|---|
| **A** | Progression | ( ) | **B** Tedium | ( ) |
| **C** | Effective planning | ( ) | **D** Knowledge | ( ) |

**2** What do goals help to increase within you?

_____

**3** What are long-term goals made up of? Tick the correct option.

**A** Intermediate and short-term goals ( )

**B** Intermediate and long-term goals ( )

**C** Short-term and long-term goals ( )

**D** Short-term goals only ( )

**4** Goals are said to be SMART. Fill in the missing words to complete the following. The first one has been done for you.

S = Specific

M = _____

A = AGREED and _____

R = REALISTIC and _____

T = TIME- _____

## Motivation

**5** Fill in the missing words to complete the following sentences.

**a)** _____ motivation comes from outside you and spurs you on.

**b)** _____ motivation comes from inside you and reflects your will to win.

**6 a)** Arousal affects motivation. What does too little arousal lead to?

_____

**b)** What does too much arousal lead to?

_____

# Training Threshold

## Worthwhile Training

**1** What two things must training be to be worthwhile work?

**a)** _____ **b)** _____

**2** What can too high a work rate result in? Tick the correct options.

**A** Injury ⬭ **B** Karvonen ⬭

**C** $CO_2$ debt ⬭ **D** $O_2$ debt ⬭

**3** What does the term TTR stand for? Tick the correct option.

**A** Training Threshold Ratio ⬭

**B** Training Threshold Rate ⬭

**C** Testing Threshold Ratio ⬭

**D** Testing Threshold Rate ⬭

**4** Is the following statement **true** or **false**?

TTR is work done aerobically. _____

**5** What care should you take when establishing maximum heart rate?

_____

**6** Fill in the missing words to complete the following sentences.

The TTR is sometimes referred to as the _____ or training zone. At this level the

intensity of effort will be most _____ .

## Oxygen Debt

**7** What type of work is done if training is done above the TTR?

_____

**8** What does a build-up of lactic acid cause?

_____

**9** What substance is essential to break down lactic acid in the body?

_____

# Aerobic and Anaerobic Training

## Aerobic Training

**1** Circle the correct options in the following sentences.

Aerobic training should be moderately strenuous and done **for prolonged periods / in short bursts**. It should be carried out at approximately the TTR level and use the **smaller / larger** muscle groups.

**2** What two things happen to breathing during aerobic training?

a) .................................................................... b) ....................................................................

**3** What is increased heart size called? Tick the correct option.

**A** Myocardia ⬭

**B** Biocardia ⬭

**C** Bradycardia ⬭

**D** Tachycardia ⬭

**4** What effect does aerobic training have on lung capacity?

## Anaerobic Training

**5** Circle the correct options in the following sentences.

Anaerobic training should be very strenuous and be done **for prolonged periods / in short bursts**. It should be done **above / below** the TTR level and include lots of rest and recovery periods.

**6** What is hypertrophy? Tick the correct option.

**A** Increasing muscle size ⬭

**B** Increasing breathing rate ⬭

**C** Increasing lung capacity ⬭

**D** Increasing recovery periods ⬭

**7** During anaerobic training, which stores are used to produce energy? Tick the correct option.

**A** Glucose ⬭

**B** Lactic acid ⬭

**C** Fat ⬭

**D** Oxygen ⬭

# Training Methods

## Ways of Training

**1** Fill in the missing words to complete the following sentence.

All training methods consist of activities and need to be organised into ......................................

or ...................................... .

**2** Why are different intensity levels used in training?

......................................................................................................................................

......................................................................................................................................

## Weight Training

**3** What do the exercises focus on in weight training?

......................................................................................................................................

......................................................................................................................................

**4** What produces the overload in weight training?

......................................................................................................................................

......................................................................................................................................

**5** How is strength promoted in weight training? Tick the correct option.

**A** High resistance and high reps ⬭     **B** High resistance and low reps ⬭

**C** Low resistance and high reps ⬭     **D** Low resistance and low reps ⬭

**6** How is endurance promoted in weight training? Tick the correct option.

**A** High resistance and high reps ⬭     **B** High resistance and low reps ⬭

**C** Low resistance and high reps ⬭     **D** Low resistance and low reps ⬭

**7** Circle the correct options in the following sentences.

**a)** **Isometric / Isotonic** weight training is when muscle contraction **does / doesn't** produce movement. The load is held for approximately 5 seconds before relaxation. This develops **strength rather than endurance / both stamina and strength**.

**b)** **Isometric / Isotonic** weight training is when muscle contraction **does / doesn't** produce movement. Movement is repeated and rapid. This develops **strength rather than endurance / both stamina and strength**.

**8** Give two effects that weight training can have on muscles.

**a)** ...................................................................................................................................

**b)** ...................................................................................................................................

## Circuit Training

**1** Circuits are of two types. One is for fitness; what is the other for?

_____

**2** In a fitness circuit, each exercise concentrates on a different _____ part, so there's

an overall _____ distribution of work.

**3 a)** Design a circuit to improve fitness, showing the exercises that would be included.

**b)** How is it possible to prevent boredom in circuit training?

_____

_____

## Effects of Circuit Training

**4** Fill in the missing words to complete the following sentences.

Circuit training can improve strength and endurance, muscle _____ and posture

and _____ level. Circuit training can increase _____ density

and _____ rate, and can decrease body _____ percentage.

# Training Methods

## Interval Training

**1** What are the two main parts of interval training?

**a)** ................................................................ **b)** ................................................................

**2** Give four ways that it's possible to increase the load in interval training.

**a)** ................................................................ **b)** ................................................................

**c)** ................................................................ **d)** ................................................................

## Continuous Training

**3** Continuous training is known as LSD. What does this mean? Tick the correct option.

**A** Light slow distance running ◯ **B** Light short distance running ◯

**C** Leisurely slow distance running ◯ **D** Long slow distance running ◯

**4** What is not included in continuous training?

................................................................................................................................

**5** **a)** What type of fitness does continuous training mainly improve and is mostly suited to?

................................................................................................................................

**b)** Give an example of the kind of activity continuous training is mostly suited to.

................................................................................................................................

**6** Where did Fartlek training first come from? Tick the correct option.

**A** Sweden ◯ **B** Slovenia ◯

**C** Spain ◯ **D** Italy ◯

**7** How does Fartlek training differ from continuous training?

................................................................................................................................

................................................................................................................................

**8** In what two ways can the load be increased in Fartlek training?

**a)** ................................................................................................................................

**b)** ................................................................................................................................

# Training Methods

## Flexibility Training

**1** What is flexibility training a series of?

.......................................................................................................................................................

.......................................................................................................................................................

**2** Complete the following sentence.

The emphasis in flexibility training is on ....................................................................................

.......................................................................................................................................................

.......................................................................................................................................................

**3** Fill in the table to show the three types of flexibility stretching and how each one is performed.

| Type of Flexibility Stretching | How it is Performed |
|---|---|
| a) | |
| b) | |
| c) | |

**4** Give four advantages of flexibility training.

a) ..............................................................................................................................................

b) ..............................................................................................................................................

c) ..............................................................................................................................................

d) ..............................................................................................................................................

# Programmes of Exercise

## Exercise Programmes

**1** **a)** Exercise programmes help to promote fitness and concentrate on the ............................. aspect of exercise.

**b)** Exercise programmes concentrate on a number of specific fitness ............................. and tend

not to need much ............................. .

## Aerobic Programmes

**2** What type of fitness is aerobics a form of?

.............................................................................................................................

**3** Is the following statement **true** or **false**?

Equipment is essential for an aerobics session. .............................

**4** How can intensity be introduced into step aerobics?

.............................................................................................................................

**5** What equipment is essential for aqua aerobics?

.............................................................................................................................

**6** Why is aqua aerobics good for the overweight?

.............................................................................................................................

.............................................................................................................................

## Body Conditioning Programmes

**7** What does Pilates include in addition to stretch and mobility work?

.............................................................................................................................

**8** Fill in the missing word to complete the following sentence.

Yoga is a conditioning programme that aims to unify physical performance with

a ............................. approach.

## Seasonal Sports

**1** Fill in the table to show the four main sections of a performer's year and what happens.

| Section of Year | What Happens |
|---|---|
| a) | |
| b) | |
| c) | |
| d) | |

## Training Venues

**2** Where do elite performers often like to train? Tick the correct options.

A   At high altitude ◯

B   At low altitude ◯

C   Warm places ◯

D   Cold places ◯

## Periodisation

**3** Fill in the missing words to complete the following sentences.

Periodisation is the method of organising training within blocks of _____.

These are training programmes with _____ and _____ goals.

## Peaking

**4** Is the following statement **true** or **false**?

Training should reflect the competition calendar. _____

**5** In a training programme, when are peaks aimed for?

_____

# Training Sessions

## Training Times

**1** What should a training session be? Give three examples.

**a)** .......................................................................

**b)** .......................................................................

**c)** .......................................................................

**2** What does a warm-up phase reduce the possibility of?

.......................................................................

## Training Phases

**3** Give three stages a warm-up phase could include.

**a)** .......................................................................

**b)** .......................................................................

**c)** .......................................................................

**4** Fill in the missing words to complete the following sentence.

The fitness or exercise phase should maintain ........................... and gradual

........................... .

**5** What happens to lactic acid during the warm-down phase?

**A** It stays in the blood ⬜

**B** It's stored for future use ⬜

**C** It's flushed out ⬜

**D** Nothing ⬜

**6** Is the following statement **true** or **false**?

The warm-down phase does not repay the oxygen debt. ...........................

**7** Why is any extra blood removed from the muscles?

.......................................................................

.......................................................................

# Effects of Exercise

## Long-Term Effects of Exercise

**1** Give the four major effects that long-term exercise has on the circulatory system.

**a)** ........................................................................................................

**b)** ........................................................................................................

**c)** ........................................................................................................

**d)** ........................................................................................................

**2** What effect does long-term exercise have on the following?

**a)** Chest ..............................................................................................

**b)** Vital capacity ................................................................................

**c)** Gas exchange ................................................................................

**d)** Bones ..............................................................................................

**e)** Ligaments ......................................................................................

## Temperature Regulation

**3** What is the core body temperature? Tick the correct option.

**A** 35 degrees Centigrade ⬭

**B** 36 degrees Centigrade ⬭

**C** 37 degrees Centigrade ⬭

**D** 38 degrees Centigrade ⬭

**4** What does it mean when a blood vessel vasodilates? Tick the correct option.

**A** Gets bigger ⬭      **B** Gets smaller ⬭

**C** Joins together ⬭    **D** Disappears ⬭

**5** Circle the correct options in the following sentences.

In order to maintain core temperature in cold conditions, blood vessels under the skin **vasoconstrict / vasodilate** and heat loss is **increased / reduced** by radiation. The muscles shiver, causing heat energy to be released via **respiration / inspiration** in cells.

# Effects of Exercise

## Short-Term Effects of Exercise

**1** What does increased muscle action need more of when exercise takes place?

    **A** Lactic acid ⬭

    **B** Energy ⬭

    **C** Tidal volume ⬭

    **D** Carbon dioxide ⬭

**2** What effect does short-term exercise have on the respiratory rate, body temperature, heart rate, stroke volume and blood pressure? Tick the correct option.

    **A** They all increase ⬭

    **B** They all decrease ⬭

    **C** They all stay the same ⬭

**3** Fill in the missing words to complete the following sentence.

During exercise, blood is diverted away from the _____ and intestines and directed

to the _____ .

## General Effects of Exercise

**4** What effect does exercise have on a highly trained performer? Tick the correct options.

    **A** Higher fitness levels are maintained ⬭

    **B** Motor skills become fine tuned ⬭

    **C** A slower recovery rate takes place ⬭

    **D** There's a faster recovery time from illness and injury ⬭

**5 a)** What happens to fitness levels in the average performer?

_____

_____

**b)** What happens to fitness levels in the below average performer?

_____

_____

## Tests for Fitness

**1** Give two examples of what the results of pre and post tests show.

**a)** ........................................................................................................................

**b)** ........................................................................................................................

**2** Choose the correct words from the options given to complete the sentences below.

**validity**                    **protocol**

**a)** All tests must measure what they set out to measure – this is called ........................................ .

**b)** All tests should be carried out in the same way every time – this is called test

........................................ .

## Tests of Strength

**3** What are the following equipment or methods used to measure?

**a)** Grip dynamometer

........................................................................................................................

**b)** Tensiometer

........................................................................................................................

**c)** Standing long jump

........................................................................................................................

## Tests for Suppleness

**4** What is the sit and reach test used to test for? Tick the correct option.

**A** Mobility at the hips ⃝

**B** Mobility at the lower back ⃝

**C** Back and leg strength ⃝

**D** Explosive leg strength ⃝

# Testing

## Tests for Local Muscular Stamina

**1** What do the following tests measure?

**a)** Press-ups

.......................................................................................................................................................

**b)** Sit-ups

.......................................................................................................................................................

## Tests for Cardiovascular Fitness

**2** Fill in the missing words to complete the following sentence.

Cardiovascular fitness is referred to as cardiovascular ........................................., aerobic

......................................... and aerobic ..........................................

**3** What happens in the Harvard step test?

.......................................................................................................................................................

.......................................................................................................................................................

.......................................................................................................................................................

.......................................................................................................................................................

**4** **a)** What kind of test is the Cooper test? Tick the correct option.

    **A** Maximal test ◯

    **B** Sub-maximal test ◯

**b)** How is the Cooper test performed? Tick the correct option.

    **A** Run for 5 minutes as far as possible ◯

    **B** Run 5 miles in 12 minutes ◯

    **C** Run for 5 minutes, stop, then run for 5 minutes ◯

    **D** Run for 12 minutes as far as possible ◯

**5** What is the bleep test, or multi-stage fitness test, also known as?

.......................................................................................................................................................

# Testing

## Tests of Speed and Skill

**1** Fill in the missing words to complete the following sentence.

Agility is a combination of _____ and change of _____.

**2 a)** Name a test that measures agility.

**b)** Briefly explain how the test works.

## Tests for Reaction

**3 a)** Name a test that measures reaction.

**b)** Briefly explain how the test works.

## Tests for Balance

**4 a)** Name a test that measures balance.

**b)** Briefly explain how the test works.

# Factors Affecting Performance

## Physique

**1** Give the three names used when establishing somatotype.

**a)** .............................................................................................................................................................

**b)** .............................................................................................................................................................

**c)** .............................................................................................................................................................

**2** Draw and label a somatotype chart. Show where the following athletes are likely to be placed:

**a)** High jumper

**b)** Gymnast

**c)** Sumo wrestler

## Age and Gender

**3** Fill in the missing words to complete the following sentences.

**a)** Age affects performance. In younger years, performance levels can be ............................................ .

**b)** As we get older, performance levels ............................................ . In later years, performance levels are

at their ............................................ .

**c)** During male puberty, ............................................ is produced to make boys bigger and stronger.

During female puberty the ............................................ becomes wider for future child birth.

# Factors Affecting Performance

## Environment

**1 a)** Give four environmental factors that could affect performance.

**i)** ......................................................................................................

**ii)** ......................................................................................................

**iii)** ......................................................................................................

**iv)** ......................................................................................................

**b)** What effect should these factors have on where to train for a competition?

......................................................................................................

......................................................................................................

**2** Give two examples of what humidity affects during performance.

**a)** ......................................................................................................

**b)** ......................................................................................................

## Illness and Injury

**3** Circle the correct option in the following sentence.

Many injuries are associated with specific sports, which can be caused by the **nurture / nature** of the game.

**4** Is the following statement **true** or **false**?

Being fit prevents illness. ....................................

**5** Fill in the missing words to complete the following sentence.

Injuries can be caused by a ............................... of fitness or readiness for

............................... .

**6** What can happen if you return too quickly after injury?

......................................................................................................

......................................................................................................

# Factors Affecting Performance

## Diet and Nutrition

**1** Choose the correct words from the options given to complete the sentences below.

| greater | less | stable |
|---|---|---|
| gain | loss | excess |

**a)** Daily intake equals energy expenditure equals _____ weight.

**b)** Daily intake _____ than energy expenditure equals weight

_____.

**c)** Daily intake less than energy expenditure equals weight _____.

## The Healthy Heptagon

**2** Draw a Healthy Heptagon, including the names of the essential components of a balanced diet.

# Factors Affecting Performance

## Special Diets

**1** What is carbo-loading?

_____

_____

**2** What will athletes of strength events often eat more of? Tick the correct option.

**A** Olives ⬭  **B** Protein ⬭

**C** Carbohydrate ⬭  **D** Calcium ⬭

## Lifestyle

**3** Fill in the following table with the three types of well-being and a brief description of each.

| Type of Well-Being | Description |
|---|---|
| a) | |
| b) | |
| c) | |

**4** Draw lines between the boxes to match the lifestyle factor with how it affects performance.

| Lifestyle Factor | How it Affects Performance |
|---|---|
| Attitude | Can lead to poor health |
| Diet | Needs to be ample and of good quality |
| Alcohol | Correct balance needed |
| Sleep | Positive approach to performance |

**5** What three main aspects should a performer's lifestyle include?

a) _____  b) _____  c) _____

# Skill

**1** Choose the correct words from the options given to complete the sentences below.

> **minimum**       **maximum**       **predetermined**       **learned**

Skill is a _____ response. It is a _____ movement pattern

performed with the _____ of outlay and effort.

**2** What is a complex skill made up of?

_____

**3** What type of skill is it where you decide when to perform? Tick the correct option.

    **A**   Open       ◯

    **B**   Internal paced       ◯

    **C**   Closed       ◯

    **D**   External paced       ◯

## Guidance     OCR

**4** What is guidance?

_____

_____

**5** Fill in the following table with the three types of guidance and a brief description of each.

| Type of Guidance | Description |
|---|---|
| **a)** | |
| **b)** | |
| **c)** | |

## Learning Skills OCR

**1** Using the tennis serve as an example, show how a skill is learned in parts.

**a)** _____

**b)** _____

**c)** _____

**d)** _____

**2** **a)** What is fixed practice?

_____

_____

**b)** How might a golfer apply fixed practice?

_____

_____

_____

## Feedback OCR

**3** What does the term KP mean? Tick the correct option.

**A** Knowledge of Perfection ⬚     **B** Knowing some Performance ⬚

**C** Knowledge of Performance ⬚     **D** Knowledge of Physicality ⬚

**4** What does the term KR mean? Tick the correct option.

**A** Knowledge of Results ⬚     **B** Knowing some Results ⬚

**C** Knowledge of Resolution ⬚     **D** Knowledge of Respite ⬚

**5** Give a brief definition of KP.

_____

_____

**6** Name the two sources of feedback.

**a)** _____     **b)** _____

# Drugs in Sport

## Acceptable Drug Use

**1** Give three examples of drugs that are acceptable in sport.

a) _____

b) _____

c) _____

## Unacceptable Drug Use

**2** **a)** Anabolic steroids are sometimes used by performers. Give two ways that performers might benefit from their use.

i) _____

ii) _____

**b)** Give three negative side effects from anabolic steroid use.

i) _____

ii) _____

iii) _____

**3** **a)** What effect do beta-blockers have on a performer? Tick the correct option.

A  Narcotic  ⬭               B  Relaxant  ⬭

C  Stimulant  ⬭              D  Diuretic  ⬭

**b)** Name a sport in which beta-blockers might be considered effective.

_____

**4** **a)** What effect can taking diuretics have on a performer?

_____

_____

**b)** Name a sport where diuretics might be used.

_____

## Unacceptable Drug Use (cont.)

**1** Give four effects that stimulants might produce.

a) ................................................................................................................................

b) ................................................................................................................................

c) ................................................................................................................................

d) ................................................................................................................................

**2** Give two physical effects that alcohol might produce.

a) ................................................................................................................................

b) ................................................................................................................................

**3 a)** Why might some performers smoke tobacco? Tick the correct option.

A  It's a narcotic ◯     B  It's a relaxant ◯

C  It's a stimulant ◯     D  It's a diuretic ◯

**b)** Give three conditions that smoking tobacco can lead to.

i) ................................................................................................................................

ii) ................................................................................................................................

iii) ...............................................................................................................................

**4** Fill in the missing words to complete the following sentence.

When blood doping is practiced, blood is removed from the performer. The blood is

.............................................. and the red cells are .............................................. just before the race.

**5 a)** What does EPO stand for? Tick the correct option.

A  Ethylprotein ◯     B  Erythropoietin ◯

**b)** What effect does EPO have on the body?

................................................................................................................................

................................................................................................................................

◯

# Taking Part

## Leisure Time

**1** Choose the correct words from the options given to complete the sentences below.

| **labour** | **internet** | **retirement** | **flexible** | **travelling** |

a) Leisure time has increased owing to more _____ saving devices and reduced

_____ times to and from work.

b) _____ home shopping, people taking early _____ and people

having a more _____ or part-time work pattern are also factors.

## Leisure Time Use

**2** How does age affect how we spend leisure time?

_____

_____

_____

**3** Fill in the missing words to complete the following sentences.

a) Activities learned at _____ can direct you towards sports you know and enjoy.

b) The _____ and _____ models encourage you to take part in sport, rather than just watch.

**4** Give two examples of how the place where you live can influence the activities you do.

a) _____

_____

b) _____

_____

**5** What do governments do to encourage us and make us aware of healthy lifestyles?

_____

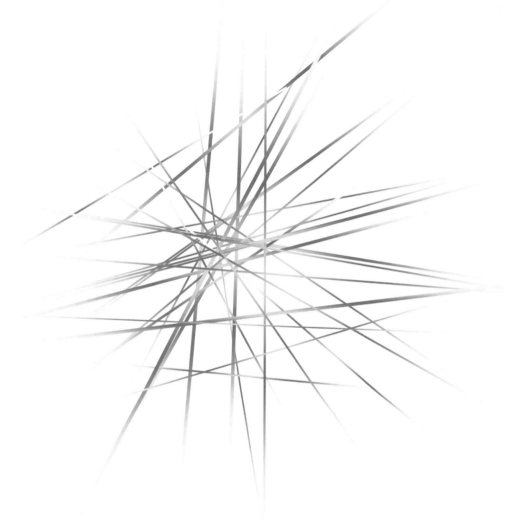

# ESSENTIALS

## GCSE Physical Education
### Workbook Answers

## Body Systems

### Page 4

1. A; B; F; G

2. a) walk
   b) shape; organs

3. B

4. a) Long
   b) Flat
   c) Short
   d) Irregular
   e) Long

5. A2; B1

6. Appendicular

### Page 5

1. D

2. a)–d) **In any order:** Cervical; Lumbar; Thoracic; Sacral

3. The bones are fused together.

4. cartilage

5. a) D
   b) Move in all directions

6. a)–c) **In any order:** Support; Movement; Protection

### Page 6

1. Fibrous – Fixed
   Cartilaginous – Slightly movable
   Synovial – Freely movable

2. a)–e) **In any order:** Hinge; Pivot; Ball and Socket; Saddle; Condyloid

3. A1; B3; C4; D2

4. False

### Page 7

1. Flexion – Joint closing. Extension – Joint opening / straightening. Adduction – Towards centre of body. Abduction – Away from centre of body. Rotation – Turning round. Circumduction – Drawing a circle.

2. Flexion – Hinge; Ball and socket; Condyloid; Saddle. Extension – Hinge; Ball and socket; Condyloid; Saddle. Abduction – Ball and socket; Condyloid; Saddle. Adduction – Ball and socket; Condyloid; Saddle. Rotation – Ball and socket; Pivot. Circumduction – Ball and socket.

3. a) Tendons
   b) Ligaments

4. **Any two suitable answers, e.g.** Inflammation; Arthritis; Osteoarthritis; Lupus

### Page 8

1. a) i)–iii) **In any order:** Voluntary; Involuntary; Cardiac
   b) Cardiac

2. A8; B11; C4; D3; E6; F1; G2; H7; I9; J5; K10

3. Agonist – Contracts to create movement
   Antagonist – Relaxes to allow movement
   Synergist – Stabilises joint

### Page 9

1. a) Fast twitch fibres are powerful, work and react quickly, but tire fast.
   b) **Any suitable answer, e.g.** Sprints; Speed events

2. a) Slow twitch fibres work in a slow, steady, sustained manner and tire less quickly.
   b) **Any suitable answer, e.g.** Endurance events; Marathons

3. a) stay same length; don't move
   b) change length; move

4. The muscles get shorter and the fibres lengthen.

5. The muscle fibres lengthen under tension.

6. a) B
   b) A

### Page 10

1. a)–c) **In any order:** Nasal passages; Wind pipe (trachea); Lungs

2. a) They pull the ribs forward and upward.
   b) It pulls down.

3. a)–b) **In any order:** Intercostal muscles pull the ribs down and in; The diaphragm is pulled up.

4. transfer; lungs; capillaries

5. a) Oxygen; red; uptake
   b) Carbon dioxide; capillaries; alveoli

### Page 11

1. A; B; E; G; H

2. The maximum amount of air you can breathe in and out.

3. a) low; oxygen; energy
   b) carbon dioxide; water; long; rest
   c) high; glucose
   d) lactic; debt

4. a) Glucose + Aerobic oxygen = Carbon dioxide + water
   b) Glucose = Lactic acid + a bit of Energy

### Page 12

1. figure; eight

2. a)–c) **In any order:** Heart; Blood; Blood vessels

3. A3; B2; C5; D7; E9; F1; G10; H4; I8; J11; K6; L12

4. a) Left ventricle
   b) Right atrium

### Page 13

1. A pressure wave

2. D

3. C

4. Wrist

5. a) systemic
   b) pulmonary

6. a) arteries; elastic
   b) veins; elastic
   c) arteries / veins; veins / arteries; narrow; cell; exchange

### Page 14

1. Sphygmomanometer

2. B; C

3. a)–d) **In any order:** Plasma; Red cells; White cells; Platelets

4. Heat – From the muscles to the skin
   Waste products – From all body tissue to the kidneys
   Oxygen – From the lungs to all body tissue
   Carbon dioxide – From body tissue to the lungs
   Nutrients – From the small intestine to all parts of the body.

5. a) Lymphocytes
   b) Platelets
   c) Phagocytes

6. Clotting

### Page 15

1. a) increase; increases; increases
   b) lower; faster

2. a) increase; oxygen
   b) fibres; capillaries
   c) deoxygenated

3. False

4. a) soft organs; muscles
   b) surface; skin; heat

## Fitness and Training

### Page 16

1. a)–d) **Any four from:** To promote and improve health; To promote and improve fitness; To obtain social benefits; To obtain mental benefits; To obtain physical benefits.

2. a) meet people
   b) spirit
   c) status
   d) rewarding
   e) earn money

3. a) stress; tension
   b) stimulation
   c) self-confidence
   d) perspective; fun
   e) goal

### Page 17

1. a) True
   b) False
   c) False

2. a) well-being
   b) efficiently; motor

3. A

4. The ability to meet the physical demands of a sporting activity.

5. a)–e) **In any order:** Strength; Speed; Stamina; Suppleness, Somatotype

### Page 18

1. a)–c) **In any order:** Static; Explosive; Dynamic

2. The shortest time taken to move a body or body part a specific distance.

3. strenuous; long

**4. a)–b) In any order:** Muscular endurance; Cardiovascular fitness

**5.** C

**6. a)–b) In any order:** Flexibility; Mobility

**7.** Aerobic fitness – For lower intensity activities; Long periods of time; Gets energy from oxygen
Anaerobic fitness – For higher intensity activities; Short periods of time; Gets energy from glucose

**Page 19**

**1.** Motor fitness is the ability to perform successfully in a given sporting activity.

**2. a) In any order:** speed; strength
   **b)** ability; direction
   **c)** co-ordination
   **d)** position
   **e)** stimulus
   **f)** psychological

**3.** vertebrae

**4.** Good posture puts less strain on other muscles and joints and avoids the joints straining.

**5.** A; B; D

**Page 20**

**1.** Deterioration

**2. a)** activity
   **b)** increase
   **c)** reducing, stopping completely
   **d)** boring; changing training methods

**3.** Intensity

**4.** F – How often you exercise
   I – How hard you exercise
   T – How long you exercise
   T – Which exercises are suitable to your chosen sport

**5.** Muscles lose their tone and size.

**Page 21**

**1.** A; C

**2.** Self-confidence

**3.** A

**4.** S = Specific
   M = Measurable
   A = AGREED and ACHIEVABLE
   R = REALISTIC and RECORDABLE
   T = TIME-PHASED

**5. a)** Extrinsic
   **b)** Intrinsic

**6. a)** Low performance levels
   **b)** Poor performance levels

**Page 22**

**1. a)–b) In any order:** Strenuous; Effective

**2.** A; D

**3.** B

**4.** True

**5.** Work under supervision

**6.** target; effective

© **Letts and Lonsdale**

**7.** Anaerobic

**8.** Fatigue

**9.** Oxygen

**Page 23**

**1.** for prolonged periods; larger

**2. a)–b) In any order:** It becomes deeper; It becomes fuller

**3.** C

**4.** It increases lung capacity

**5.** in short bursts; above

**6.** A

**7.** C

**Page 24**

**1. In any order:** repetitions; sets

**2.** To suit the needs of the activity

**3.** Different muscle groups

**4.** Increasing the resistance

**5.** B

**6.** C

**7. a)** isometric; doesn't; strength rather than endurance
   **b)** isotonic; does; both stamina and strength

**8. a)–b) In any order:** Increase strength; Increase size; Increase tone

**Page 25**

**1.** Skill

**2.** body; balanced

**3. a)**

   **b)** A variety of exercises can be included and circuits can be organised for indoor or outdoor use.

**4.** tone; skill; bone; metabolic; fat

**Page 26**

**1. a)–b) In any order:** Work; Rest

**2. a)–d) In any order:** Increase duration; Increase intensity; Increased work periods; Reduced rest

**3.** D

**4.** Rest periods

**5. a)** Aerobic
   **b) Any suitable answer, e.g.** Marathon running

**6.** A

**7.** It has high and low intensity periods.

**8.** Increase intensity; Extend high intensity periods

**Page 27**

**1.** Mobility exercises at specific joints

**2.** Increasing the range of movement at joints

**3. a)–c) In any order:** Passive static – Movement supplied by partner; Passive active – Movement supplied by performer; Ballistic – Use of body momentum.

**4. a)–c) In any order:** Cheap; Needs little equipment; Easy to do; Supports playing a wide range of activities.

**Page 28**

**1. a)** fun
   **b)** components; equipment

**2.** Cardiovascular

**3.** False

**4.** Increase the height of the step

**5.** Swimming pool

**6.** Water supports the body weight

**7.** Static strength work

**8.** mental

**Page 29**

**1. a)–d) In any order:** Closed / off season – Rest and recovery;
   Out of season – Aerobic / strength training;
   Pre-season – Fitness and skill training;
   Playing – competition

**2.** A; C

**3.** time; medium / long-term; long-term / medium

**4.** True

**5.** To correspond with specific competitions

**Page 30**

**1. a)** Interesting
   **b)** Useful
   **c)** Suitable to the participant

**2.** Injury

**3. a)–c) Any three suitable answers, e.g.** Light exercises; Mobility work; Pulse raisers

**4.** progression; overload

**5.** C

**6.** False

**7.** To prevent blood pooling in the veins, which can make the athlete dizzy or weak.

**Page 31**

**1. a)–d) In any order:** Heart gets bigger; Resting rate gets lower; Stroke volume increases; Red cell count increases

**2. a)** Gets bigger
   **b)** Increases
   **c)** Improves
   **d)** Become stronger
   **e)** Become stronger

**3.** C

**4.** A

**5.** vasoconstrict; reduced; respiration

1. B

2. A

3. stomach; muscles

4. A; B; D

5. a) Higher levels of fitness and performance are prepared for.
   b) Basic fitness levels improve quickly.

**Page 33**

1. a)–b) **In any order:** If progress is being made; If the training method is effective.

2. validity; protocol

3. a) Grip strength
   b) Back and leg strength
   c) Explosive leg strength

4. B

**Page 34**

1. a) Arm and body strength and endurance
   b) Abdominal strength and endurance

2. stamina; power / capacity; capacity / power

3. The subject steps on and off a box 40cm high for 5 minutes, at a rate of 30 steps per minute.

4. a) A
   b) D

5. Progressive shuttle run test

**Page 35**

1. speed; direction

2. a) Illinois agility run
   b) The subject is timed over a pre-designed pathway under specific protocols.

3. a) Rule drop test
   b) A ruler is dropped without warning and the subject must catch it as soon as possible.

4. a) Stork stand test
   b) Subject stands on one foot with their other foot against the side of the opposite knee, hands on hips. Timing starts when eyes close and stops when eyes open or subject loses balance.

### Factors Affecting Performance

**Page 36**

1. a)–c) **In any order:** Mesomorph; Endomorph; Ectomorph

2.

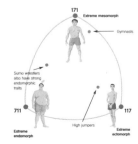

3. a) higher
   b) decrease; lowest
   c) testosterone; pelvis

**Page 37**

1. a) i)–iv) **In any order:** Altitude; Weather; Pollution; Humidity
   b) Training should reflect the proposed venue.

2. a)–b) **In any order:** Temperature regulation; Dehydration

3. nature

4. False

5. lack; participation

6. Poor performance and further injuries.

**Page 38**

1. a) stable
   b) greater; gain
   c) loss

2.

**Page 39**

1. Eating lots of carbohydrates for two or three days before competition to increase endurance.

2. B

3. a)–c) **In any order:** Physical – Body working well and free from injury; Mental – Relaxed attitude; Social – Settled social environment.

4. Attitude – Positive approach to performance
   Diet – Correct balance needed
   Alcohol – Can lead to poor health
   Sleep – Needs to be ample and of good quality

5. a)–c) **In any order:** Work / school; Physical exercise; Time to relax

**Page 40**

1. learned; predetermined; minimum

2. A number of basic skills.

3. B

4. The help received when learning a new skill.

5. a)–c) **In any order:** Visual – What you see; Verbal – What you are told; Manual – What you feel.

**Page 41**

1. a) Learn to throw the ball up
   b) Learn how to grip the racket
   c) Learn how to swing the racket
   d) Learn foot position

2. a) The repeated practice of a closed skill, regardless of environmental conditions.
   b) Practising their golf swing in all types of conditions.

3. C

4. A

5. How well you performed, regardless of your finishing position.

6. a)–b) **In any order:** Internal; External

**Page 42**

1. a)–c) **In any order:** Asthma treatment; Hayfever treatment; Drugs prescribed for illness and injury

2. a) i)–ii) **In any order:** Muscle growth; Muscle repair
   b) i)–iii) **Any three from:** Heart problems; Excess aggression; Blood pressure problems; Male characteristics develop in females; Possible loss of fertility

3. a) B
   b) **Any suitable example, e.g.** Archery; Shooting

4. a) Short term weight loss
   b) **Any suitable example, e.g.** Boxing; Wrestling; Judo

**Page 43**

1. a)–d) **In any order:** Increase alertness; Reduce fatigue; Increase competitiveness; Increase aggression.

2. a)–b) **Any two from:** Aggression; Reduced glycogen levels; Kidney damage; Liver damage

3. a) B
   b) i)–iii) **Any three from:** Blocked arteries; Excessive coughing; Emphysema; Cancer

4. frozen; re-injected

5. a) B
   b) It artificially stimulates the production of excessive red cells.

### Participation in Sport

**Page 44**

1. labour; travelling; internet; retirement; flexible

2. As people get older they participate in fewer activities. Age brings disabilities that can affect participation.

3. a) school
   b) media; role

4. a)–b) **Any two suitable examples, e.g.** Boating in coastal and river regions; Countryside offering outdoor pursuits, i.e. walking, climbing.

5. They promote health and fitness campaigns.

**Page 45**

1. a) B; C; E; G; H
   b) **Any suitable answer, e.g.** It helps you to look and feel good; it can aid recovery from illness; it is good to be part of a team; it can satisfy your competitive nature.

2. a) Family can provide an early introduction to a sport; provide encouragement and support.
   b) The desire to be involved in the same activities as friends; some activities may be perceived as 'cooler' than others by that social group.
   c) Gender stereotypes can make it easier or harder for males or females to get involved with certain sports; physical differences mean they're better suited to certain sports.

**d)** Tradition can mean that individuals from different regions / cultures are exposed to different sports.

**e)** Popularity can increase exposure and create an interest to become involved.

### Page 46

1. **a)** A4; B3; C1; D2
   **b) i)–ii) Any suitable answer, e.g.** Age; Fashion; Schools; Climate.

2. **a)** washed; bacteria
   **b)** gum
   **c)** hair; nails
   **d)** sweat; smell

### Page 47

1. C

2. B

3. **a)** B; C; E; G
   **b)** Keep feet clean and dry and dry between toes after showering.

4. **a)** B; D; E; F
   **b)** Use a verucca sock to prevent others becoming infected and apply an ointment to the affected area. In severe cases, see a doctor or chiropodist.

5. **a)–c) In any order:** Corns; Bunions; Blisters

### Page 48

1. **a)** C
   **b) i)–iii) Any three suitable answers, e.g.** Tennis; Badminton; Squash.
   **c)** Each player can challenge another player who is (a limited number of places) above them in the ladder. If they win, they will move up the ladder.

2. **a)** A league system requires each team to play a fixture against every other team in the league.
   **b)** A league system awards points for wins, draws and sometimes losses.
   **c)** If teams are level on points, their position in the table is decided by goal difference or the number of wins.

3. **a) Any suitable answer, e.g.** There is the opportunity to improve over time.
   **b) Any suitable answer, e.g.** It takes a long time to get the final result.

4. The best players / teams are seeded to make sure they meet in the later stages of the competition.

### Page 49

1. **a)** organisation; safety
   **b)** national; local

2. A; C; D; F

3. **a)–b) Any two suitable answers, e.g.** To ensure the safety of competitors; To ensure fair play.

4. A2; B3; C1

### Page 50

1. **a)** A2; B1; C4; D3
   **b) Accept any suitable answer, e.g.** Improved landing mats in the high jump.

2. **a) Any suitable example, e.g.** To show if a cricketer was run out.

**b)** To provide instant feedback to help decision-making, e.g. who crossed the winning line first.
**c) Accept any other suitable answer, e.g.** Large screens provide a better view for spectators.

### Page 51

1. **a)** To monitor level of effort and / or assess and track fitness.
   **b)** To analyse performance and help improve skills.

2. **Accept any suitable suggestion.**

3. **a)** Training / coaching tips.
   **b)** To provide information, e.g. about fixtures, rules, etc.
   **c)** To help practise / memorise / test set pieces.

4. **a) Any suitable answer, e.g.** It can help the gymnast put together / visualise / learn a routine.
   **b) Any suitable answer, e.g.** It doesn't provide any skills practice.

### Page 52

1. **a)** C
   **b) i)–iii) Any suitable answer, e.g.** Skiing – clothes must be warm and waterproof; Allow freedom of movement; Be bright or dark colours for visibility.

2. **a)–d) Any suitable answer, e.g.** Pads in cricket; Gum shields in rugby; Shin pads in football; Head guards in cycling.

3. **a)** insulators
   **b)** It helps prevent muscular strains.

4. **a)** Boots
   **b)** Spikes

### Page 53

1. hazardous; risks; check; surface; clothing

2. **a)** Risk assessment
   **b)** Warm-up

3. **a)–c) Any three from:** Make sure the surface is clear; Make sure the surroundings are safe; Make sure equipment is in good condition; Make sure the correct equipment is available; Make sure players are dressed appropriately.

4. **a) i)–ii) Any suitable answer, e.g.** Gymnastics; Trampolining; Weightlifting.
   **b)** Artistic gymnastics
   **c)** Trampolining

### Page 54

1. **a) i)–iii) Any three suitable answers, e.g.** Make sure throwing areas are clearly marked and caged; Sound a warning before each throw; Do not run to collect javelins; Waiting participants must wait behind the thrower.
   **b)** Rake them to keep them level and clear of debris. Always put the rake in a safe place afterwards.

2. **a)** The pool side will be wet, slippy and hard. You could slip and injure yourself.
   **b) Any one from:** So that you don't get out of your depth; So that you don't dive in the shallow end.

**c) Any one from:** To avoid injuring other pool users; To avoid diving into water that is unsafe, e.g. too shallow.
**d)** Approved artificial aids have been tested for safety.

3. **a)–d) In any order:** Weather; Personal equipment; Safety equipment; Route.

### Page 55

1. **a)** bend; bent
   **b)** close to; straight
   **c)** leg; up
   **d)** without

2. **a) i)** ✗ **ii)** ✓ **iii)** ✗ **iv)** ✗
   **b) i)** Javelins should not be carried horizontal to the ground.
   **ii)** The correct method is shown. Heavy objects should be carried by two people, with their arms bent.
   **iii)** A single person should not try to lift a heavy object alone.
   **iv)** You should bend your knees and keep your back straight when lifting.

## Issues in Sport

### Page 56

1. A; C; E; G

2. **a)–b) Any two suitable answers, e.g.** The public image of the company improves; Sales increase.

3. **b)–e) In any order:** Event; Sport; Team; Individual.

4. **a)–b) Accept any two from:** Equipment; Clothing; Accessories; Transport / travel; Training costs; Expenses; Scholarships.

### Page 57

1. **a)** B; C; F; G; J
   **b)** Because they are more popular, so they attract more media coverage and a larger audience.

2. **a) i)–v) Any five suitable answers, e.g.** Aids development; Reduces financial pressures; Funds events; Provides coaching / equipment; Increases income.
   **b) i)–iii) Any three suitable answers, e.g.** Risk element; Media coverage may reduce; Wrong image presented.

3. **a) In any order:** Tobacco; Alcohol.
   **b)** Because they conflict with the values that sport promotes.

### Page 58

1. Television – G; Newspapers – F; Internet – A; Radio – E; Video / Film – B; Magazines – C; Books – D.

2. A; D; E

### Page 59

1. Sponsorship, which is a form of advertising, relies on media coverage to be successful. The Media can also be sponsors.

2. **a)** BBC; supporters; accessible; money; event
   **b)** benefit; exclusive; coverage; subscribers

3. a) i)–ii) **Any two from:** Promotes and popularises the sport; Generates finance through sponsorship; Informs and instructs; Develops technical innovations to provide better coverage; Raises awareness and interest; Creates star performers; Increases worldwide audiences.
   b) **Any suitable answer, e.g.** It can intrude on an athlete's personal life.

## Page 60

1. Moscow – 1980 – The USA led a boycott in protest over the USSR invasion of Afghanistan.
   Mexico City – 1968 – Black US athletes protested against poor civil rights.
   LA – 1984 – The USSR boycotted the games in retaliation for the US boycott at the previous games.
   Melbourne – 1956 – Spain and Holland withdrew to demonstrate their opposition to Russia's invasion of Hungary.
   Munich – 1972 – Arab nationalists took Israeli athletes hostage.
   Berlin – 1936 – Hitler refused to acknowledge the success of a black athlete.

2. a) D
   b) B
   c) Abolish apartheid.

## Page 61

1. C

2. introduced; good causes; sports clubs; good causes.

3. a) councils; facilities
   b) promotes
   c) sport; compulsory; curriculum
   d) television; seen

4. a)–b) **In any order:** sporting disasters; youth activity.

5. **Any suitable answer, e.g.** To ensure safety standards are maintained.

## Page 62

1. a) bad
   b) good
   c) bad
   d) bad
   e) good;
   f) good
   g) bad

2. C

3. A3; B4; C1; D2

4. D

## Page 63

1. a) i)–iii) **In any order:** Buying tickets; Buying merchandise; Membership subscriptions.
   b) i)–iii) **In any order:** They require special facilities; The club has to pay for marshals and extra policing; Clubs can be fined for poor behaviour.

2. influence; motivate; home; supporters; advantage

3. put off; isn't; unfairly; result

4. a) i)–ii) **Any two suitable answers, e.g.** Hillsborough tragedy in 1989; Heysel in 1985.

b) i)–iii) **Any three from:** Removal of perimeter fences; All-seater stadiums; Fan segregation; CCTV; Police forces share intelligence about troublemakers.

## Page 64

1. A4; B3; C1; D2.

2. D

3. B; D

4. a) The standard of the sport has gradually improved.
   b) Wimbledon Tennis Tournament.

## Page 65

1. They were in fact being paid, so the rules were being 'bent'.

2. A; C; D; F

3. D

4. Illegal cash payments were made by putting money into the players' boots in the changing room.

5. **Any suitable answer, e.g.** So they can compete in amateur competitions.

6. C

7. Women's professional sport is behind men's; the cash rewards are much smaller.

## Page 66

1. C

2. A; C; E

3. a)–b) **Any two from:** Physical activity is for men only; It is unattractive and unladylike for women to race around; Strenuous exercise is inappropriate; Women should stay at home and look after the family.

4. a) clothing; easier
   b) sports / games
   c) domestic
   d) worked; money
   e) healthy

## Page 67

1. D

2. a)–b) **In any order:** Sport for All; Come Alive in 75.

3. C

4. Attitudes were more liberal, so clothing could be worn that was less restrictive.

5. **Accept any two suitable examples, e.g.** Cheryl Robson; Jane Couch; Dame Kelly Holmes.

6. B, D; E

## Page 68

1. positive; can; can't

2. a) B
   b) C

3. D

4. a)–c) **Any three from:** Wider parking bays; Ramp access; Automatic doors; Appropriate changing and toilet areas; Lifts and wider corridors.

5. **Any suitable example, e.g.** The provision of competitions; Development of special equipment; Adapting the rules.

6. B

## Page 69

1. a) nineteenth; religion; Sunday
   b) C

2. **Any suitable answer, e.g.** Dress code.

3. Curling – Scotland; Cricket – England; Rugby – Wales; Hurling – Ireland.

4. C; D; E; G

### Organisation and Structure of Sport

## Page 70

1. students; compulsory; curricular; achievements

2. D

3. Outside school hours.

4. a)–c) **Any three from:** The facilities available; The school's specialisation; The attitudes of the teaching staff; Access to specialist coaching.

5. a)–c) **Any three suitable subjects, e.g.** Science; Food technology; Drama; ICT; Health education.

6. a) Physical; Education; School; Sport; Club-links.
   b) PESSCL is trying to increase the number of young people playing sport outside school, by building links between schools and local clubs.

## Page 71

1. Non-Profit Organisations – Include local authorities, voluntary schemes and sport councils.
   Private Enterprises – Private companies within the leisure and fitness industry, run gyms and clubs for a profit.
   Contracted Companies – Private companies contracted to run local authority facilities.

2. a) C
   b) i)–ii) **Any two suitable answers, e.g.** National Trust / Countryside Agency, provide leisure pursuit opportunities.

3. **In any order:** Public accessibility; Price.

## Page 72

1. The members.

2. a)–b) **Any two from:** Recreational / social aspect; Access to training / coaching; Access to facilities; Entrance into competitions; Sports development opportunities.

3. Individuals – Club competitions – Regional competitions – County competitions National competitions – International competitions.

4. A4; B3; C2; D1

## Page 73

1. a) National Governing Body
   b) B

2. B; D; E; F

**3. a)** Central Council for Physical Recreation
   **b) i)–ii) Any two from:** To promote the development of sport and physical recreation; To support specialist sports bodies; To develop award schemes; to act as a consultative body to the sports councils; To be the collective voice of sport.

**4.** Local sports club – Regional / County Governing Bodies – NGB – CCPR

### Page 74

**1. a)** Foundation ➔ Participation ➔ Performance ➔ Excellence
   **b)** Family and Friends ➔ Teachers / coaches ➔ Advanced coaches ➔ National top level coaches ➔ Individual personal coach / trainer

**2. a)** Sport England; Sport Wales; Sport Scotland; Sport N Ireland.
   **b) i)–ii) Any two from:** Support elite performers; Oversee doping control, ethics and sport science; Promote international status; Coordinate all organisations within the national framework.

### Page 75

**1.** A; C; D

**2.** Quasi-Autonomous Non-Governmental Organisation

**3.** 5; 2012; 1 000 000; 16; 25; 25; 5.

**4. a)–d) In any order:** Bisham Abbey; Lilleshall; Holme Pierrepont; EIS Sheffield

### Page 76

**1. a)** British Olympic Association
   **b)** International Olympic Committee
   **c)** International Sports Federation
   **d)** British Paralympic Association

**2. a)** A; D; F
   **b)** BOA

**3.** A3; B1; C5; D2; E4

### Page 77

**1. a)** D
   **b) i)–ii) Any two from:** Government taxes; Broadcasting rights and sponsorship; Private investment; Earned income.
   **c)** B

**2.**

**3.** A

**4.** National Lottery ➔ Sport England ➔ NGB ➔ Local Club

### Exam-Style Questions

### Pages 78–79

### Multiple Choice Questions

1.  a
2.  c
3.  b
4.  b
5.  a
6.  b
7.  c
8.  c
9.  a
10. a
11. c

### Pages 80–86

### Short Answer Questions

12. Right and left atria

13. Femur

14. Front upper arm

15. Oxygen; Carbon dioxide

16. Standing long jump; Standing high jump

17. Dynamic; Static

18. Arteries; Veins; Capillaries

19. League; Knockout; Ladder

20. Endomorph; Ectomorph; Mesomorph

21. Frequency; Intensity; Time; Type

22. Lilleshall; Holme Pierrepont; Bisham Abbey; EIS Sheffield

23. Specificity; Overload; Progression; Reversibility

24. **Any four from:** Fats; Protein; Water; Carbohydrates; Vitamins; Minerals; Fibre

25. **a)** Less strenuous; Recreational
    **b)** Injury; Infirmity
    **c)** Fun

26. **a)** Pressure wave in the blood
    **b) Any two from:** Wrist; Neck; Groin; Foot
    **c)** Low resting rate; Quick return to resting rate; Wide range

27. **a)** Stamina
    **b) Any two from:** LSD; Continuous; Step aerobics

28. **a) Any suitable example, e.g.** FA; EBBA
    **b) Any three suitable examples, e.g.** Advertising; Sponsorship; Fees; Sales
    **c) Any two suitable examples, e.g.** To improve the game; To adapt the game; Demands of media

29. **a)** Members
    **b) Any two suitable examples, e.g.** Capital grants; Recurring costs
    **c) Any three suitable examples, e.g.** Raffles; Membership fees; Gate money; Bar sales; Prize money

30. **a) Any suitable example, e.g.** Riding events; Badminton
    **b) Any two suitable examples, e.g.** Social benefits; Friendship; Fun

31. **a)** Unacceptable political situation
    **b)** Meeting to ban South Africa from the Commonwealth Games and to stop sporting contact
    **c) Any three suitable examples, e.g.** 1936 Nazism; 1956 Russian invasion of Hungary; 1972 taking of hostages; 1980 Russian invasion of Afghanistan

32. **a)** British Olympic Association
    **b) Any two from:** Pick British teams; Foster Olympic ideal; Assist with financial and technical support
    **c) Any three from:** Select venues for Games; Approve the sports to be included; Promote sporting ethics; Oppose political and commercial abuse

33. **a)** Free time
    **b)** For fun; To keep fit

34. **a) i)** A combination of speed and ability to change direction
    **ii) Any suitable example, e.g.** Rugby; Gymnastics
    **b) i)** Fast and repetitive
    **ii) Any suitable example, e.g.** Weightlifting; Cycling; Rowing

35. **a)** Stamina / strength
    **b)** Fixed load – Continuous work for a given time
    Individual load – Own level of work established

36. **a)** Mesomorph
    **b) Any one from:** Muscular; Broad shoulders; Strength and stamina
    **c)** Low reps and high load

37. **a)** Closed
    **b)** Fixed practice
    **c)** It's not possible to break down skill.

38. **a)** Learned response of a predetermined movement done with minimum effort
    **b)** Complex skills
    **c)** Visual; Verbal; Manual

### Pages 87–88

### Analysis

39. **a)** The circuit has a good range of activities with a good combination of activities.
    **b)** Strengths – All body parts catered for
    Weaknesses – Wrong order of events; Some parts follow on
    **c)** Rearrange the order of events to avoid fatigue of one body part. Change back raiser as it is not easy to measure.

40. **a)** Stamina and some speed
    **b)** LSD – aerobic, covers long distances
    Fartlek – aerobic, covers speed changes for rests
    Interval – work periods can be extended and rest periods reduced
    **c)** Short term goals to establish basic levels of fitness;
    Medium term goals to show progression towards longer distance;
    Long term goal to be able to cover distance non-stop.
    **d)** Periodisation

## ACKNOWLEDGEMENTS

The author and publisher are grateful to the copyright holders for permission to use quoted materials and images.

Every effort has been made to trace copyright holders and obtain their permission for the use of copyright material. The authors and publishers will gladly receive information enabling them to rectify any error or omission in subsequent editions. All facts are correct at time of going to press.

Letts and Lonsdale
4 Grosvenor Place
London SW1X 7DL

School orders:                    015395 64910
School enquiries:                 015395 65921
Parent and student enquiries: 015395 64913
Email:       enquiries@lettsandlonsdale.co.uk
Website:   www.lettsandlonsdale.com

ISBN 978-1-906415-41-9

01/281108

Published by Letts and Lonsdale

© 2009 Lonsdale, a division of Huveaux Plc.

British Library Cataloguing in Publication Data.

A CIP record of this book is available from the British Library.

Book concept and development: Helen Jacobs
Author: Don Webster
Project Editor: Robert Dean
Cover Design: Angela English
Inside Concept Design: Helen Jacobs and Sarah Duxbury
Text Design and Layout: Dragon Digital
Artwork: Letts and Lonsdale
Printed and bound in Italy

Letts and Lonsdale make every effort to ensure that all paper used in our books is made from wood pulp obtained from well-managed forests, controlled sources and recycled wood or fibre.

**Workbook Answers**

**GCSE Physical Education**

These workbook answers are for the new GCSE Physical Education specifications and are suitable for students starting the course from September 2009 onwards. If you started the course before this date (e.g. in September 2008), you will be following a different specification and need the workbook answers shown here instead:

Buy online at **www.lettsandlonsdale.com**

9781905129331

## Reasons to Take Part

**1** **a)** Which of the following statements provide positive reasons for participating in sport? Tick the correct options.

**A** It can be expensive to buy the necessary equipment ◯

**B** It's a social activity that can build friendships ◯

**C** It contributes to good health ◯

**D** It can result in injury ◯

**E** It's enjoyable ◯

**F** It can be hard work and exhausting ◯

**G** It can give a sense of achievement ◯

**H** It can relieve stress ◯

**b)** Give one more positive reason for taking part in sport.

## Influences on Taking Part

**2** For each of the following factors, describe one way in which it might influence an individual's choice of sporting activity.

**a)** Family

**b)** Peer Group / Friends

**c)** Gender

**d)** Tradition

**e)** Popularity

# Participation

## Participation Factors

**1 a)** The table contains four factors that affect which sports an individual participates in. Match statements **A**, **B**, **C** and **D** with factors **1–4** in the table. Enter the appropriate number in the boxes provided.

|  | Factors |
|---|---|
| **1** | Environment |
| **2** | Accessibility |
| **3** | Attitude |
| **4** | Finance |

**A** Concession rates and subsidies can help to stop this factor from excluding certain individuals.

**B** This factor will determine whether or not an individual wants to participate in a particular sport. It may be influenced by family, peers, role models or social trends.

**C** This factor can mean that certain sports are not available to individuals unless they're prepared to travel.

**D** It's important for venues to improve this factor so that more individuals can participate, including those with disabilities.

**b)** Name two other factors that might affect which sport(s) an individual participates in.

**i)** _____   **ii)** _____

## Health and Hygiene

**2** Fill in the missing words to complete the following sentences.

**a)** Clothing should be _____ after taking part in a sport to help prevent

_____ spreading.

**b)** In some sports, _____ shields should be worn to protect the teeth.

**c)** For contact sports, long _____ should be tied back and _____

should be kept clean and short.

**d)** It's important to shower after taking part in sport because _____ provides

a breeding ground for bacteria, which can cause you to _____.

## Foot Health and Hygiene

**1** During exercise the body sweats. What does a deodorant do? Tick the correct option.

    **A** Prevents the body from sweating ◯     **B** Kills bacteria ◯

    **C** Masks the smell ◯     **D** All of the above ◯

**2** Poor hygiene in sport can increase the risk of illness. What is the purpose of a vaccination? Tick the correct option.

    **A** To prevent injury ◯     **B** To protect you against catching a disease ◯

    **C** To cure a disease ◯     **D** All of the above ◯

**3 a)** Which of the following statements about athlete's foot are true? Tick the correct options.

    **A** It's caused by a virus ◯     **B** It's a fungal infection ◯

    **C** It's found in warm, moist places ◯     **D** It can't be cured ◯

    **E** It can cause itching ◯     **F** It only affects runners ◯

    **G** It causes the skin to peel and crack ◯

  **b)** How can athlete's foot be prevented?

 

 

**4 a)** Which of the following statements about verrucas are true? Tick the correct options.

    **A** They're a fungal infection ◯     **B** They're caused by a virus ◯

    **C** They usually occur on the arms ◯     **D** They're contagious ◯

    **E** They're warts on the feet ◯     **F** They can be painful ◯

    **G** They can be fatal ◯

  **b)** What should you do if you get a verruca?

 

 

 

**5** List three common problems caused by ill-fitting shoes.

  **a)** _____   **b)** _____   **c)** _____

# The Way to Play

## Competitions

**1** **a)** What type of sports usually employ a ladder system? Tick the correct option.

**A** Team sports ⬭        **B** Water sports ⬭

**C** Individual sports ⬭        **D** Non-competitive sports ⬭

**b)** Name three specific sports that use a ladder system.

**i)** _____ **ii)** _____ **iii)** _____

**c)** Explain how a ladder system works in sport.

_____

_____

_____

_____

**2** Complete the following sentences about how the league system of competition works.

**a)** A league system requires each team to play a fixture…

_____

**b)** A league system awards points for…

_____

**c)** If teams are level on points, their position in the table is…

_____

**3** Give one advantage and one disadvantage of the league system of competition.

**a)** Advantage

_____

**b)** Disadvantage

_____

**4** Seeding often takes place in a knockout system of competition. Explain who is seeded and why.

_____

_____

## Sporting Behaviour

**1** Circle the correct options in the following sentences.

**a)** By obeying the rules, players assist in the **organisation / invention** of the game and ensure the **suspension / safety** of all concerned.

**b)** Rules are established by **local / national** organisations, but may be adapted to suit **local / national** needs.

**2** Which of the following are effective methods of rule enforcement? Tick the correct options.

**A** Deducting points ◯

**B** Ignoring the rule break ◯

**C** Giving the opposition an advantage, e.g. a penalty kick ◯

**D** Suspending a player ◯

**E** Waiting until after the game to deal with the situation ◯

**F** Issuing a fine ◯

**G** Allowing the opposition to behave in the same way ◯

**3** Give two reasons why players must obey the rules.

**a)** ............................................................................................................................

**b)** ............................................................................................................................

## Sports Etiquette

**4** The table contains three terms associated with sporting behaviour. Match statements **A**, **B** and **C** with the terms **1–3** in the table. Enter the appropriate number in the boxes provided.

|   | Term |
|---|---|
| 1 | Fair play |
| 2 | Win at all costs |
| 3 | Sporting etiquette |

**A** An attitude that often conflicts with the idea of fair play ◯

**B** An unwritten code of conduct that determines what is acceptable behaviour ◯

**C** The result of good sporting etiquette and attitudes ◯

# Modern Technology

## Equipment Advances

**1 a)** The table contains the names of four sports that have benefited from technological developments. Match the technological developments **A**, **B**, **C** and **D** with the sports **1–4** in the table. Enter the appropriate number in the boxes provided.

| | Sport |
|---|---|
| 1 | Golf |
| 2 | Marathon running |
| 3 | Sprinting |
| 4 | High jump |

**A** Sensors allow the race position of individuals to be recorded as they pass distance markers and / or the finishing post.

**B** The development of carbon fibre has led to the development of stronger and more powerful equipment, without increased weight.

**C** Safety equipment has been improved so that individuals can employ more aggressive techniques without the risk of injury.

**D** Computer links between starting equipment and timing devices allow more accurate time splits and finishing times to be recorded.

**b)** Describe one other technological development that has benefited a sport.

## Camera Technology

**2** Digital camera technology is increasingly used in sport.

**a)** Explain how digital cameras can assist a cricket or tennis umpire.

**b)** Explain how a digital camera can help officials in athletics.

**c)** Describe one other application of digital camera technology in sport.

# Modern Technology

## ICT in Sport

**1** How might the following uses of ICT in sport benefit an athlete?

**a)** A heart rate monitor _____

_____

**b)** Visual analysis software _____

_____

**2** Suggest one way in which you could use a readily available piece of ICT equipment (e.g. a digital video camera or some spreadsheet software) to help you improve your performance in one of the sports that you take part in.

_____

_____

_____

_____

## Multimedia in Sport

**3** Suggest one way in which each of the following examples of multimedia can be used in sport.

**a)** DVD / CD-ROM _____

**b)** Websites _____

**c)** Interactive software / sites _____

**4** A new piece of software is developed that allows gymnasts to choreograph routines and then watch an on-screen figure run through them.

**a)** Suggest one advantage of this type of software.

_____

_____

**b)** Suggest one disadvantage of this type of software.

_____

_____

# Training Aids

**1 a)** What is the main reason why cyclists, athletes and swimmers wear body suits? Tick the correct option.

    **A** To look good  ⬭       **B** To protect them from injury  ⬭

    **C** To reduce drag and increase speed  ⬭    **D** To support their muscles  ⬭

**b)** Name a sport and then list three factors that need to be considered when designing clothing for that sport.

Sport: _____

Factors: **i)** _____

**ii)** _____

**iii)** _____

**2** Fill in the table below, listing four pieces of safety equipment worn by players today. For each piece of equipment, name one sport in which it is used.

| Safety Equipment | Sport |
| --- | --- |
| **a)** | |
| **b)** | |
| **c)** | |
| **d)** | |

**3 a)** Circle the correct option in the following sentence.

Materials that act as **conductors / insulators** are good at keeping the body warm.

**b)** How does keeping the body warm help to prevent injuries?

_____

# Footwear

**4** Describe the type of footwear used by the following sportspeople.

**a)** Cricketer _____

**b)** Track runner _____

# Playing Safe

## Safety Considerations

**1** Fill in the missing words to complete the following sentences.

All practical activities involve _____ situations. To make them as safe as possible,

it's important to minimise the _____. To do this, you must _____

all equipment, make sure that the playing _____ is safe and ensure that you wear

appropriate _____.

**2** The statements below describe two safety processes that must be carried out before a sporting event. For each one, give the correct term for the process being described.

**a)** All potential hazards are identified and a plan is put in place to eliminate or reduce each one.

_____

**b)** The participants perform exercises that gradually stretch and loosen the muscles.

_____

## Consider the Activity

**3** List three safety rules that can be applied when preparing for any games activity.

**a)** _____

**b)** _____

**c)** _____

**4** Some sports have very specific safety requirements.

**a)** Name two sports that use spotters.

**i)** _____ **ii)** _____

**b)** In which sport are hand guards often used?

_____

**c)** In which sport could the height of the ceiling be a safety factor?

_____

# Playing Safe

## Athletics Safety

**1** In an athletics stadium, where several different sports may be taking place at the same time, safety is very important.

   **a)** List three safety rules that can be applied to throwing activities, e.g. javelin, shot put or discus.

      **i)** .......................................................................................................................

      **ii)** .......................................................................................................................

      **iii)** .......................................................................................................................

   **b)** How can the landing areas for activities like the long jump and triple jump be kept safe?

      .......................................................................................................................

      .......................................................................................................................

## Swimming Safety

**2** Four safety rules are given below, which apply to all sports carried out in a pool area, e.g. swimming, water polo and diving. For each rule, give one brief reason why it is important.

   **a)** Don't run on the pool side.

      .......................................................................................................................

   **b)** Make sure you know which is the deep end.

      .......................................................................................................................

   **c)** Only jump or dive in the designated area.

      .......................................................................................................................

   **d)** Only use approved artificial aids.

      .......................................................................................................................

## Outdoor Safety

**3** Name four things that must be checked before taking part in outdoor pursuits.

   **a)** ...........................................    **b)** ...........................................

   **c)** ...........................................    **d)** ...........................................

## Lifting and Carrying

**AQA**

**1** (Circle) the correct options in the following sentences.

**a)** When lifting equipment, always **bend / straighten** the knees and keep the arms **bent / straight**.

**b)** Keep the load **away from / close to** the body and the back **arched / straight**.

**c)** Lift using the **back / leg** muscles and keep your head **up / down**.

**d)** Don't lift equipment above your head **with / without** assistance.

**2** **a)** The diagrams below show people carrying pieces of sports equipment. Put a tick or a cross alongside each diagram to show whether the equipment is being carried correctly (tick) or incorrectly (cross).

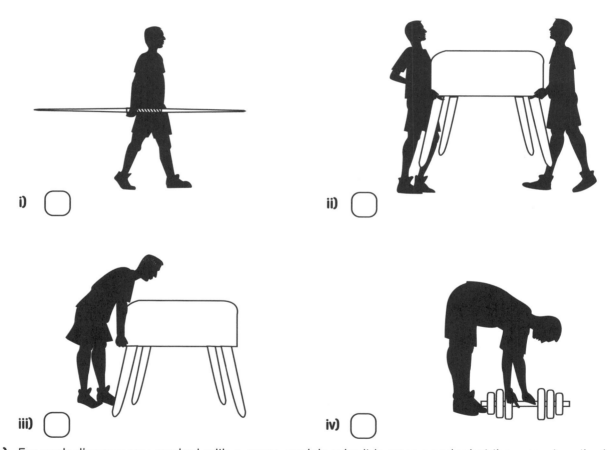

i) ☐

ii) ☐

iii) ☐

iv) ☐

**b)** For each diagram you marked with a cross, explain why it is wrong and what the correct method is.

# Sponsorship

## Sponsorship

**1** Which of the following statements about sponsorship are true? Tick the correct options.

**A** Sponsorship can provide material support ☐

**B** Sponsorship is a charitable act ☐

**C** A sponsor gains publicity ☐

**D** The sponsor provides emotional support ☐

**E** Sponsorship is a commercial transaction ☐

**F** The sport or performer has to pay for sponsorship ☐

**G** Sponsorship can provide financial support ☐

**2** Name two ways in which a company might benefit if they sponsor a successful sportsperson.

**a)** ...........................................................................................................................................

**b)** ...........................................................................................................................................

**3** List the five main recipients of sponsorship in sport. For each type of recipient, give a current example. The first one has been done for you.

**a)** Competitions, e.g. the Scottish Premier League (football league) is sponsored by The Clydesdale Bank.

**b)** ...........................................................................................................................................

...........................................................................................................................................

**c)** ...........................................................................................................................................

...........................................................................................................................................

**d)** ...........................................................................................................................................

...........................................................................................................................................

**e)** ...........................................................................................................................................

...........................................................................................................................................

**4** Sponsorship can provide the recipient with money. List two other things that a sponsor might provide.

**a)** ...................................................... **b)** ......................................................  ☐

## Obtaining Sponsorship

**1** **a)** Which of the sports listed below are most likely to attract sponsorship from large companies? Tick the **five** most likely options.

| | | | | | |
|---|---|---|---|---|---|
| **A** | Netball | ⬭ | **B** | Rugby | ⬭ |
| **C** | Football | ⬭ | **D** | Hockey | ⬭ |
| **E** | Bowls | ⬭ | **F** | Formula 1 Racing | ⬭ |
| **G** | Horse Racing | ⬭ | **H** | Archery | ⬭ |
| **I** | Fencing | ⬭ | **J** | Basketball | ⬭ |

**b)** Explain why the sports you have ticked are more likely to attract sponsorship deals from large companies.

_____

_____

_____

_____

**2** **a)** List five advantages of sponsorship for a sport.

**i)** _____   **ii)** _____

**iii)** _____   **iv)** _____

**v)** _____

**b)** List three disadvantages of sponsorship for a sport.

**i)** _____   **ii)** _____

**iii)** _____

**3** **a)** Name two types of business that sports will not accept sponsorship deals from.

**i)** _____   **ii)** _____

**b)** Why will sports not accept sponsorship from these types of business?

_____

_____

# Media

## Types of Media

**1** Draw lines between the boxes to match each type of media to the type of sports coverage it provides.

**Type of Media**

Television

Newspapers

Internet

Radio

Video / Film

Magazines

Books

**Coverage it Provides**

**A** Fast access to a large amount of information, including results, video clips, networking sites for members / supporters and educational information.

**B** Provides recorded entertainment (e.g. highlights) and educational material (e.g. coaching advice).

**C** Provides specialised or general information for a target group.

**D** Tells the stories of famous events and sports / people, e.g. biographies.

**E** Provides audio information and entertainment, including commentaries, reports and results.

**F** Provides written information and entertainment relating to current events, including results, reports, opinions and sensational stories.

**G** Provides information and entertainment in a wide range of formats, including live coverage of events, results, reports, highlights, documentaries and specific programmes for schools.

## Effects of the Media

**2** Which of the following effects of media coverage are advantages for sport? Tick the correct options.

**A** Promotes and popularises sport

**B** Forces changes to schedules

**C** Increases the pressure to succeed on players

**D** Generates financial support through sponsorship and advertising

**E** Informs, enlightens and instructs

**F** Sensationalises the use of performance-enhancing drugs

## Media and Sponsorship

**1** How are the media and sponsorship linked in their relationship to sport?

_____

_____

## Media and Conflict

**2** Choose the correct words from the options given to complete the sentences below.

| money | benefit | supporters | event | BBC |
|---|---|---|---|---|
| coverage | exclusive | accessible | | subscribers |

**a)** Some sporting events can only be covered by the _____. This benefits

_____ because it means that the event is _____ to everyone.

However, there is likely to be a limit to the amount of _____ that the

_____ can make from this type of coverage.

**b)** It can _____ a sport if two media companies get into a bidding war to buy the

rights to _____ coverage of an event, because the sport will receive a large

amount of money. However, if the television _____ can only be viewed by

_____, a lot of supporters will be unable to watch it.

**3** The interests of the media and the sport can sometimes come into conflict.

**a)** Give two reasons why media coverage is important for a sport.

**i)** _____

**ii)** _____

**b)** The media can create positive role models in sport, but it can also have a negative impact. Give one example of how the media can impact negatively on sportspeoples' lives.

_____

_____

# Politics

## Political Interference

**1** Draw lines between the boxes to match the city to the correct date and event to show how politics have affected the Olympic Games in the past.

| City | Date | Event |
|------|------|-------|
| Moscow | 1936 | Hitler refused to acknowledge the success of a black athlete. |
| Mexico City | 1972 | The USSR boycotted the games in retaliation for the US boycott at the previous Games. |
| LA | 1968 | Black US athletes protested against poor civil rights. |
| Melbourne | 1984 | The USA led a boycott in protest over the USSR invasion on Afghanistan. |
| Munich | 1956 | Spain and Holland withdrew to demonstrate their opposition to Russia's invasion of Hungary. |
| Berlin | 1980 | Arab nationalists took Israeli athletes hostage. |

**2 a)** Which country was repeatedly excluded from taking part in the Olympic Games because of the way in which it treated its black nationals? Tick the correct option.

**A** USA ◯

**B** USSR ◯

**C** Spain ◯

**D** South Africa ◯

**b)** What was the name of the agreement signed by the Commonwealth countries in 1977 that excluded this country from all sporting contact? Tick the correct option.

**A** Kyoto Agreement ◯

**B** Gleneagles Agreement ◯

**C** Glenn Agreement ◯

**D** Glenfield Agreement ◯

**c)** What did the country have to do before the ban would be lifted?

## Political Influence

**1** Which position in central government is responsible for overseeing sport in the UK? Tick the correct option.

**A** Minister for Leisure ◯          **B** Minister for Health ◯

**C** Minister for Sport ◯          **D** Minister for Fitness ◯

**2** Circle the correct options in the following sentences.

The National Lottery was **abolished / introduced** by the government. Money raised by the lottery has been used to help fund **good causes / gambling**. Some national and local **sports clubs / casinos** and venues have received this kind of financial support, because they're viewed as **good causes / money-making schemes**.

**3** Choose the correct words from the options given to complete the sentences below.

| | | | | | |
|---|---|---|---|---|---|
| promotes | businesses | curriculum | strategy | television | compulsory |
| facilities | sport | education | councils | seen | voluntary |

**a)** The government ensures that local _____ provide sports

_____ for the public.

**b)** The government _____ the country's involvement in international sport.

**c)** Acts of Parliament ensure the provision of _____ in schools and make physical

education a _____ part of the National _____ .

**d)** Some sporting events are protected from commercial _____ to ensure they can

be _____ by anyone.

**4** Name two areas linked to sport in which the government has carried out research or investigations to gain a better understanding of them.

**a)** _____          **b)** _____

**5** Give one reason why it's important for the government to pass legislation that applies to all sports facilities / venues.

_____

# Sporting Behaviour

## Sporting Behaviour

**1** Say whether the following are types of **good** or **bad** sporting behaviour.

a) Intimidating officials _____   b) Working within the rules _____

c) Disrupting the opposition _____   d) Taunting the crowd _____

e) Demonstrating etiquette _____   f) Controlling aggression _____

g) Cheating _____

**2** Which statement best describes etiquette? Tick the correct option.

A   Following the rules to the letter ◯

B   Playing to win at all costs ◯

C   Demonstrating respect for the game and your opponents ◯

D   Letting the opposition win occasionally ◯

**3** The table contains four types of bad sporting behaviour.

Match examples **A**, **B**, **C** and **D** with the terms **1–4** in the table. Enter the appropriate number in the boxes provided.

|   | Term |
|---|---|
| 1 | Over-aggression |
| 2 | Cheating |
| 3 | Gamesmanship |
| 4 | Intimidating |

A   Timewasting ◯

B   Challenging the referee's decision ◯

C   A deliberate foul ◯

D   Using unfair tactics ◯

**4** How is 'sledging' most likely to negatively affect an opponent? Tick the correct option.

A   It might cause them physical injury ◯

B   It might cause the referee to penalise them ◯

C   It might cause them to break the rules ◯

D   It might cause them to feel scared or diminish their confidence ◯

## Spectators

**1 a)** List three ways in which spectators can bring money into a sports club.

i) ..............................................................................................................

ii) ..............................................................................................................

iii) ..............................................................................................................

**b)** List three ways in which fans can cost the club money.

i) ..............................................................................................................

ii) ..............................................................................................................

iii) ..............................................................................................................

**2** Choose the correct words from the options given to complete the sentences below.

| away | players | motivate | home |
|------|---------|----------|------|
| supporters | advantage | influence | put off |

Spectators can ................................ a match in favour of their team. Cheering and clapping can

help to ................................ the team. The ................................ team is likely to have more

................................ and this can give them an ................................ .

**3** Circle the correct options in the following sentences.

Supporters might try to **put off / encourage** visiting players by shouting abuse and making loud noises.
This behaviour **isn't / is** acceptable because it can **fairly / unfairly** influence the **rules / result** of the game.

## Football Hooliganism

**4 a)** Name two instances where disruptive spectator behaviour has led to tragedy.

i) ..................................................... ii) .....................................................

**b)** List three recommendations made by the Taylor Report to help prevent future tragedies.

i) ..............................................................................................................

ii) ..............................................................................................................

iii) ..............................................................................................................

# Sporting Status

## Playing for Pay

**1** The table contains four categories of players.

Match descriptions **A**, **B**, **C** and **D** with the categories **1–4** in the table. Enter the appropriate number in the boxes provided.

| | Category |
|---|---|
| **1** | Professional |
| **2** | Shamateur |
| **3** | Semi-professional |
| **4** | Amateur |

**A** Take part for enjoyment without pay ☐

**B** Have a regular job, but are paid to play part-time ☐

**C** Playing sport is their job, for which they're paid ☐

**D** Claim to play for enjoyment, but get paid ☐

## Status

**2** Who can compete in 'open' competitions? Tick the correct option.

**A** Professionals ☐ **B** Semi-professionals ☐

**C** Amateurs ☐ **D** All of the above ☐

**3** Which of the following statements about amateur players are true? Tick the correct options.

**A** Amateur players can win cash prizes ☐

**B** Amateur players can win goods, e.g. cars, holidays and equipment ☐

**C** Amateur players receive a salary from the sports club ☐

**D** Amateur players are unlikely to be able to train and compete full-time ☐

**4 a)** How has becoming 'open' affected the standards in sports?

...........................................................................................................................

...........................................................................................................................

**b)** Which tennis event was the first grand slam to become open?

.......................................................................................... ☐

## Changes to Status

**1** In the past, some amateurs were called 'bent'. What does this mean?

**2** Which of the following statements about trust funds are true? Tick the correct options.

- **A** Amateurs can win cash prizes, which get paid into their fund ◯
- **B** Amateurs can draw a salary from their fund ◯
- **C** Amateurs can use money from their fund to cover expenses ◯
- **D** Amateurs can draw a pension from the fund when they retire ◯
- **E** Amateurs can use the fund to buy holidays and luxury items ◯
- **F** Amateurs with a trust fund retain their amateur status ◯

**3** What system did the USA develop to allow amateurs to train full-time? Tick the correct option.

- **A** Special sports loans to provide finance ◯
- **B** Contract staff to carry out their day-to-day jobs for them ◯
- **C** Free housing and food rations ◯
- **D** Sports scholarships at universities and colleges ◯

**4** Where does the term 'boot money' come from?

**5** Give one reason why a sportsperson might claim to be an amateur despite receiving payments, i.e. be a 'shamateur'.

## Changes to Sports

**6** In which year did rugby union become an open sport? Tick the correct option.

- **A** 1895 ◯
- **B** 1884 ◯
- **C** 1995 ◯
- **D** 1968 ◯

**7** What differences has professionalism had on women's sports compared with men's sports?

◯

# Discrimination

## Women in Sport

**1** Which of the following statements best describes the role of women in sport in the 1800s? Tick the correct option.

    **A**  Working class women took part in lots of team sports  ◯

    **B**  It was unheard of for women to participate in sports  ◯

    **C**  Upper-class women were able to participate in some gentle sports  ◯

    **D**  Women spent most of their leisure time in sporting pursuits  ◯

**2** In the 1800s, which sports did women take part in? Tick the correct options.

    **A**  Horse riding  ◯      **B**  Hockey  ◯

    **C**  Badminton  ◯      **D**  Netball  ◯

    **E**  Tennis  ◯      **F**  Marathon running  ◯

    **G**  Cycling  ◯

**3** Give two common views that influenced women's involvement in sport in the 1800s, which are considered old-fashioned today.

    **a)** ..............................................................................................................................

    **b)** ..............................................................................................................................

## Changing Times

**4** Fill in the missing words to complete the following sentences, which describe why attitudes towards women and sport started to change in the 1900s.

    **a)** Fashions changed and ............................... became less restrictive, making it

    ............................... for women to play sports.

    **b)** Girls were taught ............................... in schools for the first time.

    **c)** Motherhood and ............................... responsibilities were no longer seen as a barrier.

    **d)** More women ..............................., which gave them ............................... to spend on sporting pastimes.

    **e)** Viewpoints changed and sport was seen as a ..............................., social pastime for all.

## Recent Developments

**1** How did the Sex Discrimination Act affect women's participation in sports? Tick the correct option.

**A** It allowed women to become sporting amateurs but not professionals ◯

**B** It prevented women from taking part in sports ◯

**C** It allowed women to participate in some sports but not all ◯

**D** It gave women the same rights and opportunities as men ◯

**2** Name two Sports Council campaigns that promoted equal opportunities in sport.

**a)** ........................................................    **b)** ........................................................

**3** In what year was the Women's Sport Foundation established? Tick the correct option.

**A** 1884 ◯          **B** 1974 ◯

**C** 1984 ◯          **D** 1904 ◯

**4** How did changing social attitudes towards women's clothing help women to participate in more sports?

........................................................................................................................

........................................................................................................................

........................................................................................................................

## Women Today

**5** Complete the table below to give two other examples of women in sport who have become role models for other women.

| Name | Sport | Achievement |
|------|-------|-------------|
| Wendy Toms | Football | First female official for a Premier League football match |
|  |  |  |
|  |  |  |

**6** Which of the following statements about women's sport today are true? Tick the correct options.

**A** Women's sport gets the same amount of media coverage as men's sport ◯

**B** Women's sport gets less sponsorship and prize monies ◯

**C** Women can play for any sporting team if they're good enough ◯

**D** There are very few sports in which women compete directly against men ◯

**E** Women's sport is still low profile by comparison ◯

# Discrimination

## The Disabled and Sport

**1** (Circle) the correct options in the following sentence.

In sport today there is a **positive / negative** focus on what disabled people **can / can't** do rather than what they **can / can't** do.

**2** **a)** Which year was the International Year for the Disabled? Tick the correct option.

**A** 1990 ◯          **B** 1981 ◯

**C** 1996 ◯          **D** 2008 ◯

**b)** Who nominated that particular year for this purpose? Tick the correct option.

**A** The British Government ◯          **B** The Olympic Committee ◯

**C** The United Nations ◯          **D** The American President ◯

**3** Which Act made it illegal to discriminate on the grounds of disability? Tick the correct option.

**A** The Act for Inclusion ◯          **B** The Disability Discrimination Act ◯

**C** The Civil Rights Act ◯          **D** The Equal Opportunities Act ◯

**4** List three facilities that public sports venues in Britain must provide to ensure they're accessible to disabled sportspeople.

**a)** ......................................................................................................................

**b)** ......................................................................................................................

**c)** ......................................................................................................................

**5** Describe one other step that has been taken to help meet the needs of disabled sportspeople.

......................................................................................................................

......................................................................................................................

**6** Which international sporting event takes place after every Olympic Games, specifically for the disabled? Tick the correct option.

**A** The International Disabled Championships ◯

**B** The Paralympic Games ◯

**C** The Commonwealth Games for the Disabled ◯

**D** The Disability Sporting Tournament ◯

## Religion

**1** **a)** Choose the correct words from the options given to complete the sentences below.

| | | | |
|---|---|---|---|
| **Sunday** | **nineteenth** | **Saturday** | **religion** |
| | **twentieth** | **science** | |

In the late ........................................... century, ........................................... had a strong influence on

society. Because ........................................... was considered the 'Lord's Day', most sport was banned
from being played on that day.

**b)** In what year was the ban lifted for playing professional sport on a Sunday? Tick the correct option.

**A** 1908 ◯        **B** 1958 ◯

**C** 1988 ◯        **D** 2008 ◯

**2** Many people don't participate in sport on their religious holy day. Describe one other way in which faith
can restrict participation in sport.

## Ethnicity

**3** For the constituent countries of Britain, certain sports are viewed as part of their national identity. Draw
lines between the boxes to match each sport with the country it's associated with.

| Sport | Country |
|---|---|
| Curling | Ireland |
| Cricket | Scotland |
| Rugby | Wales |
| Hurling | England |

**4** If you compete in sports at an international level, which of the following factors can determine the country
that you represent? Tick the correct options.

**A** The colour of your skin ◯        **B** Your social class ◯

**C** Your country of birth ◯        **D** Your country of residence ◯

**E** Your parents' country of birth ◯        **F** Where you own property ◯

**G** Your grandparents' country of birth ◯        **H** Your ethnicity ◯

# Sport in School

## Promotion of Sport

**1** (Circle) the correct options in the following sentences.

Schools encourage their **students / teachers** to participate in sport by making physical education classes **voluntary / compulsory**, arranging extra **curricular / homework** activities, and acknowledging sporting **failures / achievements** with awards and qualifications.

**2** Which of the following sports is not included in the National Curriculum? Tick the correct option.

**A** Gymnastics ◯                    **B** Athletics ◯

**C** Swimming ◯                      **D** Scuba Diving ◯

**3** When do extra-curricular activities take place?

## School Sports Activities

**4** List three factors that will affect which sporting activities are available to students at a particular school.

**a)**

**b)**

**c)**

**5** List three subjects other than PE that help to promote health aspects in school.

**a)**                                   **b)**

**c)**

## PESSCL

**6 a)** What do the letters PESSCL stand for?

P                         E                         S

S                         C                         L

**b)** Briefly summarise what PESSCL is trying to achieve.

## Providers of Facilities

**1** Draw lines between the boxes to match the type of local provider to the correct description.

**Local Provider**

Non-Profit Organisations

Private Enterprises

Contracted Companies

**Description**

Private companies within the leisure and fitness industry, run gyms and clubs for a profit.

Private companies contracted to run local authority facilities.

Include local authorities, voluntary schemes and sports councils.

**2 a)** What kind of facilities do Sport England provide? Tick the correct option.

**A** Leisure facilities for the general public ◯

**B** Private facilities which are only open to members ◯

**C** Centres of excellence for developing elite athletes ◯

**D** Stadiums and competition venues ◯

**b)** Name two other national providers and specify the type of facilities / opportunities that they provide.

**i)** ..........

**ii)** ..........

## Location of Facilities

**3** The factors that affect the location and development of sports facilities are summarised in the '6 Ps of influence'. Which two are missing from the list below?

Population

Public needs

Planning permissions

aPpropriate surroundings

..........

..........

# Organisation of Sport

## Local Organisation of Sport

**1** Who is normally responsible for running a local sports club? .........................................................

**2** Give two advantages of becoming a member of a local sports club.

**a)** .........................................................................................................................................................

**b)** .........................................................................................................................................................

**3** Local sports clubs are seen as the first stepping stone towards international competitions. Fill in the gaps to show the structure of competitive sport.

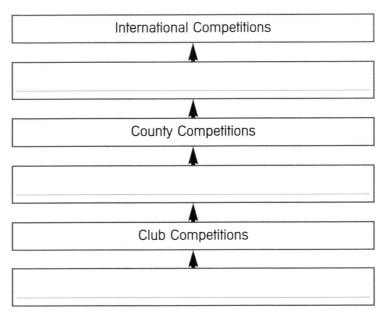

```
┌─────────────────────────────────────┐
│       International Competitions      │
└─────────────────────────────────────┘
                  ▲
┌─────────────────────────────────────┐
│                                       │
└─────────────────────────────────────┘
                  ▲
┌─────────────────────────────────────┐
│          County Competitions          │
└─────────────────────────────────────┘
                  ▲
┌─────────────────────────────────────┐
│                                       │
└─────────────────────────────────────┘
                  ▲
┌─────────────────────────────────────┐
│           Club Competitions           │
└─────────────────────────────────────┘
                  ▲
┌─────────────────────────────────────┐
│                                       │
└─────────────────────────────────────┘
```

**4** The table contains four roles within the structure of a local sports club. Match the areas of responsibility **A**, **B**, **C** and **D** with the roles **1–4** in the table. Enter the appropriate number in the boxes provided.

|   | Role |
|---|------|
| **1** | Captain |
| **2** | Secretary |
| **3** | Chairman |
| **4** | Treasurer |

**A**  Manages the finance and club accounts ⬜

**B**  The leader of the club ⬜

**C**  Organises fixtures and deals with correspondence ⬜

**D**  Leads the players ⬜

## National Organisation of Sport

**1 a)** What does NGB stand for?

N................................. G................................. B.................................

**b)** Which of the following statements about NGBs is true? Tick the correct option.

**A** There is one NGB that is responsible for all sport in the UK ☐

**B** There is an NGB for each different sport ☐

**C** NGBs have been set up for football, rugby and cricket only ☐

**D** NGBs are only concerned with professional sport ☐

**2** Which of the following duties are carried out by an NGB? Tick the correct options.

**A** Organising local social events ☐ **B** Organising local and national competitions ☐

**C** Coaching local teams ☐ **D** Drafting the rules of the game ☐

**E** Fostering links with the media ☐ **F** Selecting the team for international events ☐

**3 a)** What does CCPR stand for?

........................................................................................

**b)** State two of the main aims of the CCPR.

**i)** ........................................................................................

**ii)** ........................................................................................

**4** Complete the flow chart below to show the link between a local sports club and the CCPR.

```
┌──────────────────────────────┐
│                              │
└──────────────────────────────┘
               ▲
┌──────────────────────────────┐
│                              │
└──────────────────────────────┘
               ▲
┌──────────────────────────────┐
│                              │
└──────────────────────────────┘
               ▲
┌──────────────────────────────┐
│                              │
└──────────────────────────────┘
```

# Promoting Excellence

1. It's said that there are few elite performers but many participants.

   **a)** Complete the sports pyramid below.

   | Excellence |
   |:---:|

   |  |
   |:---:|

   | Participation |
   |:---:|

   |  |
   |:---:|

   **b)** Complete the coaching pyramid below.

   |  |
   |:---:|

   | National / top level coach |
   |:---:|

   |  |
   |:---:|

   | Teachers / club coaches |
   |:---:|

   |  |
   |:---:|

## Sports Councils

2. **a)** Complete the diagram to show the four sports councils that fall under the umbrella of UK Sport.

   **UK Sport**

   [ ]  [ ]  [ ]  [ ]

   **b)** State two of the key roles of UK Sport.

   i) _____

   ii) _____

# Promoting Excellence

## Sport England

**1** Sport England is a QUANGO. Which of the following statements about QUANGOs are true? Tick the correct options.

**A** It's set up by the government ⬭

**B** It's established by an independent committee ⬭

**C** It's funded by the government ⬭

**D** It has its own decision-making powers ⬭

**E** It's controlled by the government ⬭

**F** It's funded by private investment ⬭

**2** What does QUANGO stand for?

_____

**3** Choose the correct numbers from the options given to complete the following sentences. You may need to use each number more than once.

| 25 | 1 000 000 | 5 | 16 | 2012 |
|----|-----------|---|----|----|

Sport England has set _____ targets to be achieved by _____.

It wants to get _____ more people playing sport; reduce the drop-out rate of

_____ year olds by _____ %; improve talent development in at

least _____ selected sports; increase peoples' satisfaction in playing; and support the

delivery of _____ hours of sport per week for young people.

## National Sports Centres

**4** There are four national sports centres run by Sport England in England. Fill in the missing words to complete the list below.

**a)** _____ in Buckinghamshire.

**b)** _____ in Shropshire.

**c)** _____ in Nottinghamshire.

**d)** _____ in Yorkshire.

# Promoting International Sport

## Olympic Associations

**1** State what the letters stand for in the names of each of the following organisations.

**a)** BOA ................................................................................................................................

**b)** IOC ................................................................................................................................

**c)** ISF ................................................................................................................................

**d)** BPA ................................................................................................................................

**2 a)** Which of the following roles are carried out by the IOC? Tick the correct options.

    **A** Decide where each Olympic Games will be held ⃝

    **B** Raise money for the national team ⃝

    **C** Select team members ⃝

    **D** Approve which sports and events will take place ⃝

    **E** Organise transport and accommodation for the team ⃝

    **F** Work with the host nation to plan the Games ⃝

**b)** Which other organisation carries out the remaining roles in the list above?

................................................................................................................................

**3** The following diagram illustrates the administration of sport at international level. Match **A–E** with the labels **1–5**. Enter the appropriate number in the boxes provided.

    **A** BOA ⃝     **B** National Coaching Foundation ⃝

    **C** IOC ⃝     **D** CCPR ⃝     **E** Sports Council ⃝

## Main Sources of Income

**1** **a)** Which of the following does not provide cash funding for amateur clubs? Tick the correct option.

    **A** National Lottery ◯         **B** Sport England ◯

    **C** NGB ◯         **D** Tote ◯

**b)** List two other income sources for amateur sport.

    **i)** ..................................................     **ii)** ..................................................

**c)** What is the name given to money gained from raffles, bar takings and hospitality? Tick the correct option.

    **A** Sponsorship money ◯         **B** Earned income ◯

    **C** Expenses ◯         **D** Gross profit ◯

**2** In the diagram below, fill in the four main sources of income that a professional sports club has.

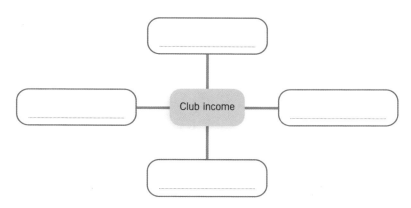

**3** What is expected to be a primary source of funding for the 2012 games? Tick the correct option.

    **A** The National Lottery ◯         **B** Public contributions ◯

    **C** Private investment ◯         **D** Taxes ◯

**4** Use the words provided to complete the flow chart and show how money from the National Lottery reaches local sports clubs.

| NGB | Sport England | Local Club | National Lottery |
|---|---|---|---|
| .................. → | .................. → | .................. → | .................. |

# Exam-Style Multiple Choice Questions

The following type of multiple choice question is offered by AQA, OCR and Edexcel. (Circle) your answer.

**1** One of the functions of the skeleton is to produce blood. Where is this done?

   **a)** Long bones

   **b)** Skull

   **c)** Phalanges

   **d)** Pelvic bones

**2** In the heart, where is the mitral valve found?

   **a)** Between the left and right atria

   **b)** Between the left and right ventricles

   **c)** Between the left ventricle and the left atrium

   **d)** None of these

**3** Which of the following pairs of bones are not found at the shoulder joint?

   **a)** Scapula and humerus

   **b)** Radius and ulna

   **c)** Clavicle and scapula

   **d)** Humerus and clavicle

**4** Which of the following is not a pulse point?

   **a)** Carotid

   **b)** Hyaline

   **c)** Femoral

   **d)** Radial

**5** Which of the following bones are not part of the appendicular skeleton?

   **a)** Ribs

   **b)** Radius

   **c)** Phalanges

   **d)** Femur

**6** In which direction is the arm travelling when it moves away from the body?

**a)** Adduction

**b)** Abduction

**c)** Extension

**d)** Flexion

**7** In which part of the vertebrae is there no movement between the bones?

**a)** Thoracic

**b)** Lumbar

**c)** Coccyx

**d)** Sacral

**8** Which of the following is not a type of muscle?

**a)** Involuntary

**b)** Smooth

**c)** Rough

**d)** Cardiac

**9** In which type of contraction do the muscle fibres stay the same length?

**a)** Isometric

**b)** Isotonic

**c)** Concentric

**d)** Eccentric

**10** Which of the following is part of the respiratory system?

**a)** Alveoli

**b)** Blood

**c)** Intercostal muscles

**d)** Articular cartilage

**11** Which of the following does not describe aerobic exercise?

**a)** Low intensity

**b)** Uses oxygen to produce energy

**c)** Produces lactic acid

**d)** Can work for long periods of time

# Exam-Style Short Answer Questions

The following type of question is offered by OCR.

12 Give the name for the two top chambers of the heart.

.................................................................................................................................................... [1]

13 Which is the longest bone in the body?

.................................................................................................................................................... [1]

14 Where are the biceps?

.................................................................................................................................................... [1]

15 Which two gases are carried by the blood?

....................................................................................................................................................

.................................................................................................................................................... [2]

16 Name two tests that measure power in the legs.

....................................................................................................................................................

.................................................................................................................................................... [2]

17 What other types of strength are there besides explosive strength?

....................................................................................................................................................

.................................................................................................................................................... [2]

18 Name the three types of blood vessels.

....................................................................................................................................................

....................................................................................................................................................

.................................................................................................................................................... [3]

19 Name three types of competition.

....................................................................................................................................................

....................................................................................................................................................

.................................................................................................................................................... [3]

# Exam-Style Short Answer Questions

**20** Name the three categories in somatotyping.

..........................................................................................................................................

..........................................................................................................................................

.................................................................................................................................. [3]

**21** What does FITT stand for?

..........................................................................................................................................

..........................................................................................................................................

..........................................................................................................................................

.................................................................................................................................. [4]

**22** Name four national sports centres in England.

..........................................................................................................................................

..........................................................................................................................................

..........................................................................................................................................

.................................................................................................................................. [4]

**23** Name the four principles of training.

..........................................................................................................................................

..........................................................................................................................................

..........................................................................................................................................

.................................................................................................................................. [4]

**24** List four components of a balanced diet.

..........................................................................................................................................

..........................................................................................................................................

.................................................................................................................................. [4]

# Exam-Style Short Answer Questions

The following types of question are common to AQA and Edexcel.

**25 a)** Give two reasons why the over-50s take part in fun running.

.................................................................................................................................

................................................................................................................................. [2]

**b)** Give two reasons why the over-50s should not take part in competitive rugby.

.................................................................................................................................

................................................................................................................................. [2]

**c)** What is the main reason for people to play recreational sport?

................................................................................................................................. [1]

**26 a)** What is a pulse?

................................................................................................................................. [1]

**b)** Give two places in the body where a pulse can be measured.

.................................................................................................................................

................................................................................................................................. [2]

**c)** Give three ways that the pulse rate can indicate fitness.

.................................................................................................................................

.................................................................................................................................

................................................................................................................................. [3]

**27 a)** Which component of fitness does aerobic training mainly improve?

................................................................................................................................. [1]

**b)** List two types of aerobic training.

.................................................................................................................................

................................................................................................................................. [2]

# Exam-Style Short Answer Questions

**28 a)** Give the name of one National Governing Body of sport.

..................................................................................................................................................... [1]

**b)** Give three ways that a NGB can raise money.

.....................................................................................................................................................

.....................................................................................................................................................

..................................................................................................................................................... [3]

**c)** Give two reasons why a NGB might change its rules.

.....................................................................................................................................................

..................................................................................................................................................... [2]

**29 a)** Who is a voluntary sports club run for?

..................................................................................................................................................... [1]

**b)** State two benefits to sport of the National Lottery.

.....................................................................................................................................................

..................................................................................................................................................... [2]

**c)** List three ways in which a sports club might raise money.

.....................................................................................................................................................

..................................................................................................................................................... [2]

**30 a)** Name one sport where men and women compete against each other.

..................................................................................................................................................... [1]

**b)** Give two benefits of men and women playing recreational sport together.

.....................................................................................................................................................

..................................................................................................................................................... [2]

# Exam-Style Short Answer Questions

**31** **a)** Why was South Africa initially banned from Olympic competition?

.................................................................................................................................................. [1]

**b)** What was the Gleneagles Agreement?

..................................................................................................................................................

.................................................................................................................................................. [2]

**c)** Give three examples of the Olympic Games being used as a political tool.

..................................................................................................................................................

..................................................................................................................................................

.................................................................................................................................................. [3]

**32** **a)** What do the letters BOA stand for?

.................................................................................................................................................. [1]

**b)** Give two functions of the BOA.

..................................................................................................................................................

.................................................................................................................................................. [2]

**c)** Give three functions of the IOC.

..................................................................................................................................................

..................................................................................................................................................

.................................................................................................................................................. [3]

**33** **a)** What is leisure time?

.................................................................................................................................................. [1]

**b)** Give two reasons why people play sport in their leisure time.

..................................................................................................................................................

.................................................................................................................................................. [2]

The following type of question is offered by AQA and Edexcel.

**34** **a)** **i)** What is meant by the term agility?

.................................................................................................................................

**ii)** Give an example of physical activity that includes this component.

.................................................................................................................................

**b)** **i)** What is meant by the term dynamic strength?

.................................................................................................................................

**ii)** Give an example of a physical activity that includes this component.

.................................................................................................................. [4]

**35** **a)** State one benefit of fitness that can be achieved through circuit training.

.................................................................................................................................

**b)** With regard to circuit training, explain the following:

Fixed load .........................................................................................................

.................................................................................................................................

Individual load ...................................................................................................

.................................................................................................................. [5]

**36** **a)** Name the body type of a boxer.

.................................................................................................................................

**b)** Give a reason why this body type is an advantage to this performer.

.................................................................................................................................

.................................................................................................................................

**c)** Which type of weight training should a boxer follow?

.................................................................................................................................

.................................................................................................................................

.................................................................................................................. [5]

**37** **a)** What type of skill is a golfer's swing an example of?

.................................................................................................................................................

**b)** State which type of practice the golfer should use.

.................................................................................................................................................

**c)** Explain why part practice would not be a suitable way to improve the golf swing.

.................................................................................................................................................

.................................................................................................................................................

.................................................................................................................................................

.............................................................................................................................. [5]

**38** Running is often described as a basic skill.

**a)** Give a definition of the term 'skill'.

.................................................................................................................................................

.................................................................................................................................................

.................................................................................................................................................

**b)** What is made up from basic skills?

.................................................................................................................................................

**c)** List the three forms of guidance that help in the learning of a new skill.

.................................................................................................................................................

.................................................................................................................................................

.............................................................................................................................. [5]

The following type of question is offered by AQA and Edexcel.

**39** The following is a proposed circuit designed to improve overall strength.

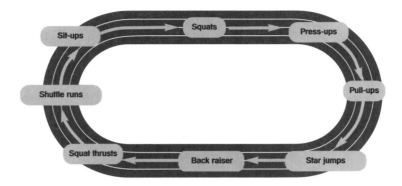

a) Evaluate the circuit in relation to its overall aim.

b) Comment on its strengths and weaknesses.

c) Describe any changes you might make and give reasons for these changes.

_____

_____

_____

_____

_____

_____

_____

_____

_____[10]

# Exam-Style Analysis Questions

**40** Mary-Jane is a fairly fit and active person in her early twenties. She decides that she wants take part in the Great North Run. This is a half-marathon over fairly flat ground run on roadways. She has nine months to prepare.

**a)** List those aspects of fitness that would need to be developed.

**b)** Briefly describe three training methods that she might use.

**c)** Explain, with examples, the types of goals she should set herself.

**d)** How can she ensure that she peaks at the right time?

[10]